D1572050

Make Your Clinics Flow with Synchrony

Make Your Clinics Flow with Synchrony

A Practical and Innovative
Guide for Physicians,
Managers, and Staff

Dennis P. Han, MD
Aneesh Suneja, MBA

ASQ Quality Press
Milwaukee, Wisconsin

American Society for Quality, Quality Press, Milwaukee 53203
© 2016 by ASQ
All rights reserved. Published 2015
Printed in the United States of America
21 20 19 18 17 16 15   5 4 3 2 1

Library of Congress Cataloging-in-Publication Data

Names: Han, Dennis, author. I Suneja, Aneesh, 1968– author.
Title: Make your clinics flow with synchrony : a practical and innovative
  guide for physicians, managers, and staff / Dennis Han, MD, Aneesh Suneja,
  MBA.
Description: Milwaukee, Wisconsin : ASQ Quality Press, 2016. I Includes index.
Identifiers: LCCN 2015043405 I ISBN 9780873899239 (hard cover : alk. paper)
Subjects: LCSH: Medical offices—Planning—Handbooks, manuals, etc. I
  Physician and patient.
Classification: LCC R728 .H353 2016 I DDC 610.68—dc23
LC record available at http://lccn.loc.gov/2015043405

ISBN 978-0-87389-923-9

Publisher: Lynelle Korte
Acquisitions Editor: Matt T. Meinholz
Managing Editor: Paul Daniel O'Mara
Production Administrator: Randall Benson

ASQ Mission: The American Society for Quality advances individual, organizational,
and community excellence worldwide through learning, quality improvement, and
knowledge exchange.

Attention Bookstores, Wholesalers, Schools, and Corporations: ASQ Quality Press
books, video, audio, and software are available at quantity discounts with bulk
purchases for business, educational, or instructional use. For information, please
contact ASQ Quality Press at 800-248-1946, or write to ASQ Quality Press,
P.O. Box 3005, Milwaukee, WI 53201-3005.

To place orders or to request ASQ membership information, call 800-248-1946. Visit our
website at http://www.asq.org/quality-press.

 Printed on acid-free paper

Quality Press
600 N. Plankinton Ave.
Milwaukee, WI 53203-2914
E-mail: authors@asq.org

ASQ The Global Voice of Quality®

*We dedicate this book to our wives
Mary Lynn Han and Cary Suneja.*

Table of Contents

List of Figures

Preface

This book is about the radical notion that the patient's time in any healthcare process is as valuable and as important to process improvement as the physician's. When the patient is seen in this light as a resource to be managed, the process can achieve what we have come to call *synchrony*. Synchrony means valuing the patient's time and the physician's time equally, bringing them together when each is ready for the other, without waste or delay. To make clinics flow, or, for that matter, any other process that joins physicians with patients, synchrony is fundamental.

For years, those of us in the process improvement field in healthcare have put physicians in a spotlight. After all, physicians are shared resources—constraints on healthcare processes—whose time has to be managed in such a way as to create flow and prevent bottlenecks. Lean tells us that every process has a *constraint*: a step that sets the pace of throughput for the process as a whole, and can create backlogs and bottlenecks when not managed properly. Find that constraint, manage its time, and we can make that process more efficient and effective. In healthcare, physicians are not only shared resources, they are the ones who create processes, wield authority, and influence the work environment of the rest of the care delivery team. It made sense to focus our attention on the roles physicians play and how to best manage their time as shared resources.

And yet, despite the attention paid to the physician as the resource to be managed, the problems and dysfunctions experienced by frontline care teams—nurses, medical assistants (MAs), technicians, and others who support the doctors—persist. We hear time and time again about interpersonal problems on care teams, problems with team communication, conflicting directions for work depending on the doctor giving the orders, competing priorities when new or emergency patients are added to an already full schedule, and frontline staff who feel like they have no voice or ability to suggest improvements. These issues are raised not just by the team involved in direct patient care, but by managers and administrators as well. As important as it is to improve the physicians' processes and focus the team's efforts on supporting those processes, those actions alone will not solve all the problems that plague teams in healthcare.

The issues described above are impossible to resolve permanently when addressed one at a time, in isolation. We cannot resolve interpersonal tensions in a broken system that distributes work unevenly, nor can we give people a voice in an environment that does not acknowledge their contributions. But when we broaden the focus of improvement efforts to include the patient's time as an equally valuable resource and work to achieve synchrony, we can fundamentally improve healthcare processes and the lives of the people who operate them. That is because when we make improvements that positively impact the physician's ability to do her job, and at the same time improve the patient experience, everyone involved sees the benefit, and a host of related problems can be solved.

We have lived the journey to synchrony from two distinctly different points of view: Dr. Dennis Han is an ophthalmologist specializing in diseases of the retina at the Medical College of Wisconsin and Froedtert Memorial Hospital; Aneesh Suneja is an engineer and lean consultant who worked with Dr. Han to transform his practice. Physicians and other healthcare providers generally are trained in the science of medical care rather than in the science of caring for patients. This is an important distinction—medical schools do not typically teach process engineering, so teaming the physician with a process improvement expert enables a transformation to take place.

Dr. Han's clinic—and indeed Dr. Han himself—experienced a truly remarkable transformation. At the end of his year-long engagement with Aneesh Suneja, his patients experienced an 85% reduction in non-value-added wait times, and a corresponding 97% "top box" rating on patient satisfaction surveys ("strongly agree to recommend this doctor's office to others"). Financially, his practice saw a 25% year-over-year increase in *relative value units* (RVU) production and a 41% increase in payments due to increased physician availability. Dr. Han, who had been stressed and headed for burnout, was able to reengage with both his patients and his team. By eliminating wasted steps, Dr. Han now has more time to spend face-to-face with his patients, and his technicians are not rushed through important quality procedures. The team works deliberately, steadily, and with fewer interruptions or periods of high stress that can lead to missed steps and errors. His patients recognize the difference.

And yet, as remarkable as this transformation is, it is not unique. We have created systems for synchrony in many different specialties and types of clinics. We know it works. If you are a physician, clinic manager, administrator, technician, or provider of health services in a clinic setting, you can use the guidelines described in this book to effect a transformation as well.

We describe what synchrony looks like and how it operates in the Introduction. Chapters 1 through 5 walk through the guidelines for achieving synchrony in any practice. Chapter 6 presents additional techniques for internal change agents facilitating process improvement with care delivery teams in a clinic setting. We recognize that no two clinics are alike, and each has its own patient needs, available space, staff, equipment, administrative constraints, and challenges. But while the individual implementation may be specific to your circumstances, the principles are universal. We include Dr. Han's story, as well as the stories of other physicians, managers, administrators, and technical staff, to illustrate the range of clinic environments that have used these principles to achieve synchrony.

After all, it is the people in the process who create change. Their stories may become your stories, retold in new and different ways by your clinic team as it seeks to make positive change.

Acknowledgments

We would like to thank those who provided support, feedback, and their expertise in developing the concepts shared in this book. Gary Colpaert, Dr. Dale Heuer, Steve Alper, Kay Kastner, and Kay Mareno made the transformation possible for Dr. Han at the Froedtert and MCW Eye Institute through their sponsorship, leadership, and on-the-ground support. At Retina Specialists of Michigan, Dr. Tom Aaberg and Dr. Scott Westhouse, working with architect Peter Baldwin of AMDG Architects and practice manager Bernie Dewey, used the concepts discussed here to design and build their new ophthalmology offices, and shared photographs and experience during the writing of this book. Special thanks to Dr. Chris Decker, Dr. Kia Saeian, Dr. Amy Franta, Mary Hansen, Rosa Sivaja, Dr. Henry Kaplan, Dr. William Nunery, and Mathieu Nunery, all of whom have tested these concepts and shared their insights over the last 10 years.

The authors especially acknowledge Cary Suneja for her invaluable editorial and creative efforts, without which this book would not have been possible.

Introduction: Definition of Synchrony

*S*ynchrony is the ability of a healthcare process to control the pace of the physician process and the pace of the patient process such that the physician and patient are ready for each other at the same time, without waste or delay. When a process achieves synchrony, the patient does not wait for the doctor, nor does the doctor wait for the patient.

Synchrony has its roots in lean philosophy. *Lean* is the name given to the Toyota Production System, first developed in Japan over the last half of the twentieth century. Today the term *lean* is shorthand for a system that focuses on the relentless rooting out of waste in processes—the wastes of excess motion, duplicative process steps, errors, and waiting. Healthcare is of course much different from manufacturing, but the principles apply to clinics as well as factories, as waste exists in many forms in nearly every process. Lean gives us a framework and toolbox for finding and eliminating waste.

Figure 1, the synchrony diagram, illustrates how synchrony works, and what components need to be in place to allow a process to achieve it. Synchrony is created by establishing a base of stable processes, creating a multifunctional team that can dynamically adjust the pace of processes, and using lean tools for continuous improvement. The clinic flows when the pace of the physician's process matches the pace of the patient's process. The term "MD flow" and the principles demonstrated could apply to activity flow of any clinician provider (DO, nurse practitioner, and so on).

PHYSICIAN AND PATIENT FLOW

Figure 1 highlights the two key flows in the clinic process—the physician flow and the patient flow—which are dependent on a base of stable processes, and adjusted in real time by multifunctional staff using a specific

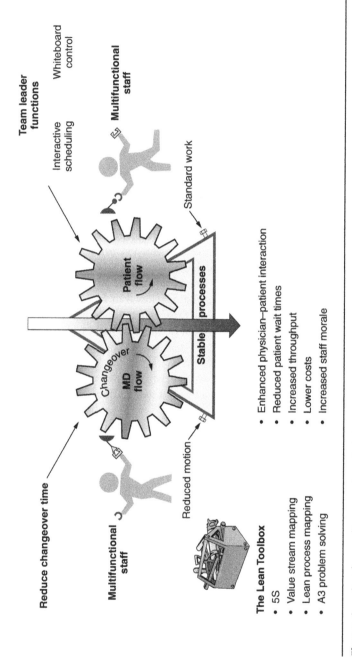

Figure 1 Synchrony diagram—target state.

set of tools and principles. The key word here is *flow*—a state in which both physician and patient move from value-added step to value-added step without interruption or delay, from door to door in the clinic. Flow happens when all clinic processes are working seamlessly, when information and resources are available as they are needed, and when the resulting calm environment is one in which the physician and patient can experience the best interaction possible.

In the diagram, the physician and patient flows are represented by the two large gears engaged in the center of the stability triangle. The goal is to synchronize provider availability with patient availability so that both gears turn smoothly. If either of the two gears stops, both stop. When the gears are not synchronized, the flow through the clinic slows or becomes erratic, leading to wasted time and effort for the provider and staff, and to waiting patients. Because of these wastes, a nonsynchronized system inherently uses more resources as it produces backups of patients that consume staff time and physical space.

The two flows must be coordinated and synchronized with *active* measures. In most clinics, the provider works as quickly as possible, with patients becoming available to him at a time largely determined by their appointment times and completion of screening tests, imaging studies, or other processes. In most clinics, no active interventions are taken to match the moment of provider availability with the moment of patient availability. Sometimes, the physician is ready but the patients are not. More often, multiple patients are available when the provider is not. A sign of a passive process is the piling of records in bins as a measure of flow, a common practice in medical clinics. This phenomenon occurs even in the era of electronic medical records, with patient tags (registration sheets, test requisitions, or their equivalent) functioning in a similar way to indicate where patients are in the process. These electronic markers "stack up" the same way paper files do, and again are an indicator of a passive system that requires both the provider and the patient to wait.

Two active measures are highlighted in Figure 1: reduced changeover times and the team leader role. *Changeover* comprises all of the process steps that occur between the conclusion of one patient consultation and the moment that the physician walks into the next exam room. From the patient's perspective, changeover is non-value-added time and often causes delays, especially if the physician uses the changeover time to make phone calls or is otherwise unavailable when the next patient is ready to be seen. Strategies for reducing changeover time are discussed in Chapter 3.

The team leader role is an important one on the care delivery team. Team leaders are not physicians; they are typically nurses or medical assistants who are responsible for providing oversight of the patient process while the clinic is running. Team leaders make sure the physician knows which patient to see next, and can allocate resources to alleviate bottlenecks in real time, using information displayed on the patient status whiteboard. The team leader is a vital part of achieving synchrony, as it is her role to direct the active measures and adjustments needed to keep the physician process synchronized with the patient process. Team leaders are discussed in Chapter 6; patient status whiteboards are discussed in Chapter 2.

Synchrony is more easily achieved in a system with little variation in task times, such as when each patient goes through an identical sequence of steps that take about the same amount of time. However, many clinics have high variation in task times and testing needs among patients, as well as a great deal of variation in the duration of physician-patient interaction. In clinics with high variation, synchronized flow is obtained by establishing dynamic processes that adjust to circumstances on a minute-by-minute basis. It requires flexibility of worker roles to adjust the pace of the process for both the physician and patient, and it requires a simultaneous, real-time awareness of patient whereabouts in the system by clinic staff members and the provider.

STABILITY

It is impossible to make improvements to an unstable process. Too often, a process owner or manager will see or read about a particular tool or idea and rush out to implement it in an environment that is unstable and chaotic. Despite good intentions, the change results in more instability and chaos rather than improvement. The critical prerequisite for positive change is a stable base of operations.

That base is represented by the base of the triangle. In the clinic setting, establishing a consistent space and work team around the physician is a critical and often underestimated aspect of achieving stability. Once the physician has a regular, consistent team assigned to support the clinic and is operating the clinic from a consistent physical space, the process can be made stable and predictable through the implementation of standard work and 5S workplace efficiency measures. Patient and staff motion can be analyzed and reduced to further reduce variation in task times that lead to waiting, an additional waste.

Further, without process stability, improvements cannot be measured. The effects of incremental change to an unstable environment are difficult to assess and can be lost amidst a sea of confusion. Making changes in an unstable environment can simply add more variation to chaos, sometimes making things worse. Stability allows the PDCA (plan–do–check–adjust) cycle of process improvement to occur. In inefficient clinics, it can be assumed that process variation is present and that wastes must be removed from the system. The tools of lean can be used to great effect to accomplish this and bring about stability upon which further improvements can be built.

THE LEAN TOOLBOX

There are some fundamental process improvement tools that the entire team needs to employ in order to begin making improvements and facilitating change. The tools are shown in the toolbox at the bottom left of Figure 1. These include:

- *5S.* A system of workplace organization and cleanliness that originated with Toyota in Japan

- *Value stream mapping.* A high-level mapping tool that identifies major process steps and sources of wasted time, motion, and effort in the process

- *Lean process mapping.* A more detailed map that captures individual process steps and critical process metrics (including elapsed time and first-time quality)

- *A3 problem solving.* A structured problem-solving process summarized on a single page (called an A3)

Value stream mapping and process mapping are discussed in Chapter 1; 5S is discussed in Chapter 6. Since A3 problem solving is a new approach to problem solving for many, we will take a closer look at it here.

A3 PROBLEM SOLVING

A3 problem solving is kind of like the "history and physical" and SOAP (subjective/objective/assessment/plan) methods of thinking that most physicians are taught in the medical evaluation of a patient. It got its name from the size of a piece of paper (designated A3 by international standards) with the same dimensions as two 8.5 x 11" sheets taped together in a side-by-side fashion. It provides a logical method of reasoning about a problem that can be communicated quickly on a single sheet of paper. It is adaptable and applicable to virtually any problem. It helps to maintain focus over potentially long periods of time and create common understanding during multiple, sometimes separate, discussions with many stakeholders in the process.

However, unlike a medical evaluation, the recordings are made in pencil and are changeable as new information or ideas are encountered. It is not a static document, but a dynamic one that changes as the understanding of the problem increases. In addition, inputs to the A3 come from multiple sources, with the coordinator of the problem-solving effort taking ownership of the A3 document. The A3 document itself is not a private document, but one that is used by its owner to engage stakeholders and to foster communication.

An example of an A3 form is shown in Figure 2. The left panel typically has a title (the issue at hand), background with a statement of the problem, current conditions, goals or future state, and analysis, including root cause analysis. The right panel shows proposed countermeasures, who is to do what action items and by what date, and follow-up measures. There are very good resources written about this useful tool; we encourage you to use the A3 to help your team focus on fact-based problem solving.

THE THEORY OF CONSTRAINTS

In addition to the tools listed above, there is an underlying concept that is critical to understanding synchrony: the theory of constraints. First introduced by Eliyahu Goldratt more than 25 years ago, the *theory of constraints* posits that in any process there is one step that limits how fast the rest of the process can be performed. That step is the *constraint*, or bottleneck, and the rest of the process should be structured around it. In other words, your system is set up to achieve a goal, but your ability to meet that goal is limited by at least one constraint.

In healthcare terms, we need to look at the concept of constraints on two levels. The first is to recognize that the physician is always a main constraint. Patients, after all, are in the clinic to see the physician. Your clinic is limited by how quickly the physician can see patients, and the clinic system should be structured to allow the physician to see patients as continuously as possible. The theory of constraints tells us that the value-producing resource—in this case the physician—should be in operation continuously, from the beginning of the workday to its end, whenever these might be. In the clinic, this means keeping a menu of activities in front of the physician at all times, without a backup or delay. It means synchronizing the physician's availability more precisely with that of the patient's to keep the physician busy and reduce the waste of waiting by both staff and

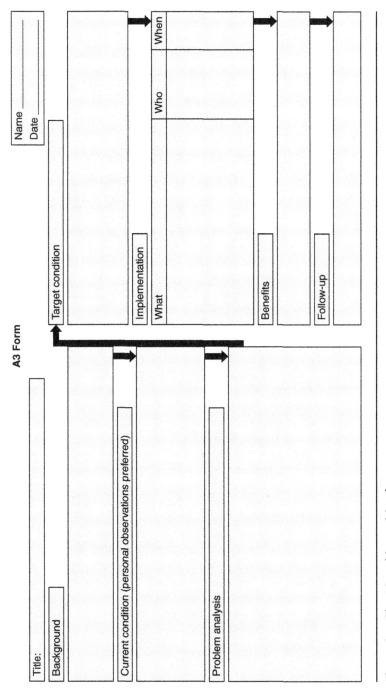

Figure 2   The A3 problem-solving form.

patients. In this model, ancillary staff do not work in absolute deference to the physician's desire to speed his own work flow; rather, the team attempts to keep both patients and physicians moving so that they are each available to each other at the same moment in time on a consistent basis.

The other level at which we need to view constraints is this: the patient is also a constraint, and should not be held up in any part of the process, but should be ready to see the physician when the physician is ready to see him. It makes no sense to room and prep more patients than the physician can see; in other words, we cannot keep patients waiting just to ensure that the physician is always busy.

This dual nature of constraints in the clinic is truly the heart of synchrony. Synchrony requires us to see *both* the physician and the patient as simultaneous and equal constraints whose time must be valued. The care delivery process must be structured around both the patient and the physician so that one matches the availability of the other, just in time. Our goal in achieving synchrony is to create a system centered around the physician and patient flows, and create enough flexibility to adjust the pace of each flow to keep them both moving at the same pace. The guidelines presented in the next chapters are designed to do exactly that: to first define the process and create a stable base of operations (Chapter 1), and then manage the patient flow (Chapter 2) and the physician flow (Chapter 3).

This principle should not be misconstrued as trying to make the physician less efficient. Ideally, anything that will shorten physician cycle time while maintaining value will also increase productivity. However, if there are constraints elsewhere in the system that limit the flow of work to the physician, this increased physician efficiency yields no additional value. For example, if the doctor is always ready for the next patient, but the patient is sometimes in X-ray and unavailable to the doctor, then no gains are made in physician efficiency. For synchrony to happen, the patient and the physician need to be ready for each other at the same time. Therefore, constraints elsewhere should be reduced to the point that the physician can be kept busy providing value all of the time.

Patient flow is the major component of these other constraints, and must be synchronized to the cycle times of the physician. What the synchrony concept adds to the theory of constraints is that the physician cycle time can be dynamically increased or decreased to allow resources to reduce these other constraints when they become rate limiting. For any given number of resources, such as number of staff or examining rooms, the ability to add this dynamic can increase productivity and reduce patient waiting times.

Many physicians intuitively understand the theory of constraints, but not the concept of synchrony. While they embrace the idea that staff should support physician activity, they may require that other clinic staff attend to their every need, even though patient flow is bogging down in steps that precede the physician-patient encounter.

Consider this scenario: physician flow at the expense of patient flow. A physician Dr. Han knows requires his staff to be present with him throughout the patient encounter as he performs minor procedure visits. During that time, they are taken away from other tasks that maintain patient flow to him. They are required to do some of the basic tasks that many other physicians do on their own. There is no flexibility to allow staff to attend to the other duties. His idea is that anything that keeps him moving must be efficient. This is most certainly true when he is the only major constraint. But he is not. Remember, synchrony defines both the physician and the patient as equal constraints whose time must be valued equally. And so, because of this physician's insistence that his staff's job is solely to keep him moving efficiently, his staff are unable to reduce constraints elsewhere to maintain even patient flow to him. Intermittent and fairly frequent periods of waiting in the clinic pod for patients to be ready for him do not register in his mind as being lost opportunity and reduced efficiency. He just sees this as him "keeping up." He attributes staff support to this perception. But in fact, every minute he waits for patients is an extra minute of patient waiting time for every patient that remains on his schedule. These minutes add up—the last patient on his schedule may experience the sum of all the physician idle time as waiting time. He has lost out on both revenue production and patient satisfaction. This has occurred because he has prioritized physician flow at the expense of patient flow.

Consider another scenario: patient flow at the expense of physician flow. At a conference during which efficiency was discussed, one physician took pride in her efficiency. If she found that clinic staff were idle while she was seeing patients, she would make sure that they did "something—anything—to keep busy." However, these staff were not directed at reducing the physician cycle time, but were instead assigned to doing other busywork. There was no mechanism established for them to step in to speed the physician, such as assisting with documentation, moving the patient, answering basic questions, or providing logistical instructions on how to arrange the next appointment, and so on. These activities reduce "internal changeover time." In this scenario the patient flow exceeded physician flow, leading to staff idle time, but there was no understanding that the physician flow could be enhanced to catch up with patient flow. In fact, each minute that they fail to reduce physician cycle time translates directly to extra patient waiting time and reduced physician productivity. This has occurred because she has given physician flow lower priority than patient flow.

Finally, consider a third scenario: physician flow and patient flow at the expense of cost. These are clinics where everything runs smoothly, but it does so because resource use is high. Every step in the process has a person dedicated to it, so no patient is kept waiting. The physician, because of his having nearly unlimited resources to help him during the patient encounter, can keep up with a high flow of patients. Both he and his patients have excellent experiences, and there is high revenue production, which the physician uses to justify his staff. But many of his workers are idle intermittently throughout the day, and he wonders why his overhead costs, which go directly to his bottom line, are high. Further, his business administrator is sounding warning bells about practice expenses. In this scenario, failure to understand synchrony has led to more resource use (and cost) than necessary. The clinic has achieved physician flow and patient flow at the expense of cost.

In each of the above scenarios, understanding synchrony as we have described it in the synchrony diagram and in the context of the theory of constraints is a key for improved physician productivity, patient satisfaction, and reduced cost.

1

Observe the Patient Process

DR. HAN'S STORY: ASYNCHRONY IN ACTION

My morning clinic was going along nicely—I had already completed the expected number of patient evaluations for that time of day, and had only a few records stacked in my bin indicating patients ready for me to see. The way my clinic system worked, I was to take the topmost record, then call the patient to the exam room and do my evaluation. That morning, I pulled the record and looked twice at the name on that record. It was my former boss, the man who hired me for my current position, the one who built this clinic from the ground up. I owed my career to this man. We liked to talk, so this might take a while. Perhaps the clinic would get behind, but I thought I could make up the time. I looked around. The techs were busy screening other patients.

The visit went as usual for us, about 20 minutes of face-to-face time, whereas the usual patient took about 10. We had a thorough discussion about the patient's eye issues as this patient was very well-informed about his conditions and asked many questions, so the appointment took longer than most. I still had to document it in the record as well. The patient was in the clinic for less than an hour—pretty good, I thought, when accounting for the 20 minutes of dilation time required before I saw the patient.

As I finished, another patient approached me, distraught. "I've been here for a long time! What's going on here? This is ridiculous!"

Continued

Continued

I apologized profusely. The patient was here for a short evaluation, one that was usually completed in 10 minutes or less, aside from dilation time. What should have been for him a 30-minute visit in total already had taken at least an hour. I had no idea that this patient had waited as long as he did. Had I known, I simply would have taken him first. What time was his appointment, anyway? I certainly didn't know from looking at the bin. I had assumed that the patient who was ready for me first, the one whose record was at the top, had the earliest appointment of the bunch. Or that perhaps a patient known to desire a quick, no-nonsense visit might be placed ahead of a longer one to spare the pain of waiting. But that was too much to hope for. No one was in charge of coordinating this. It was up to me. Was that something I should be doing?

It didn't help knowing that my unhappy patient was a pillar of the community. He had a college and athletic stadium named after him for his philanthropy. He could have been a great supporter of our clinic and its research missions. My team and I sent a letter of apology, but that patient never came back. Why should he? Our clinic had a problem—we had no way of synchronizing our care to minimize waiting. What happened that day could happen again, even on a light day.

It was ironic that because I spent some extra time with the person that built my department and institute, I lost both a patient and a potential supporter. It was a bitter pill to swallow.

The scenario Dr. Han recalls in the anecdote above is a common one. It is an example of the problems that arise when there is no system in place to actively manage both physician and patient flow, or to communicate patient status to the care team. A system designed to achieve synchrony allows the care team to adjust the pace of patient and physician flow to eliminate long wait times and the problems that arise because of them. But how do we get from the problems described above to a state of synchrony?

The first step is to develop thorough, firsthand knowledge of the patient process through direct patient observations and use that knowledge to understand what is required of the process. In this chapter, we will discuss how to conduct patient observations and collect data, what types of waste to look for, and how to use the data to analyze the distribution of work in the care delivery process.

PATIENT OBSERVATIONS AND DATA COLLECTION

Patient observations are a simple and powerful way to get an up close, first-hand look at the patient process. There is no substitute for starting here if the clinic is to achieve synchrony. In lean philosophy, improvements begin with direct observations rather than historical data or written procedures. Our job is to see with our own eyes how the process is operating, and base our future actions on that knowledge.

To conduct observations, you will need a stopwatch, paper, and pencil. Follow patients from the moment they check in until they leave the clinic. It is not necessary, of course, to follow patients into the exam room; you can observe comings and goings from a safe distance in a hallway. Remember, lean does not start by trying to improve the value-added portions of the process (like the doctor-patient interaction) but instead uncovers and removes the waste in between those value-added steps. So, a vantage point from a hallway is sufficient.

While you are observing patients, map out the process you see in action. For each process step, draw a box and capture the time the patient spends in that process step (like check-in, or rooming) and the time that elapses between patient steps. You will know a particular step has ended when the patient is waiting for the next step to begin. All of the activity that happens between periods of waiting is considered one step. Map out and capture times for at least 10 patients to get a representative sample, and for each patient answer the following questions:

- How long does it take the patient to check in?

- How long does that patient wait in the waiting area before being roomed?

- How long is the patient with someone other than the physician (medical assistant, nurse, or other)?

- How long does the patient wait before seeing the physician?

- How long does the patient spend with the physician?

- How long does the patient stay in the exam room after the physician consultation?

Figure 3 is an example of the data and process map collected during patient observations. Notice that each step is captured as a box on the map, while

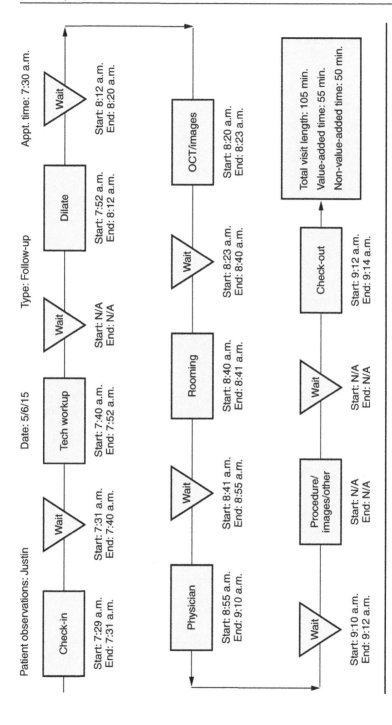

Patient observations: Justin   Date: 5/6/15   Type: Follow-up   Appt. time: 7:30 a.m.

Check-in
Start: 7:29 a.m.
End: 7:31 a.m.

Wait
Start: 7:31 a.m.
End: 7:40 a.m.

Tech workup
Start: 7:40 a.m.
End: 7:52 a.m.

Wait
Start: N/A
End: N/A

Dilate
Start: 7:52 a.m.
End: 8:12 a.m.

Wait
Start: 8:12 a.m.
End: 8:20 a.m.

OCT/images
Start: 8:20 a.m.
End: 8:23 a.m.

Wait
Start: 8:23 a.m.
End: 8:40 a.m.

Rooming
Start: 8:40 a.m.
End: 8:41 a.m.

Wait
Start: 8:41 a.m.
End: 8:55 a.m.

Physician
Start: 8:55 a.m.
End: 9:10 a.m.

Wait
Start: 9:10 a.m.
End: 9:12 a.m.

Procedure/images/other
Start: N/A
End: N/A

Wait
Start: N/A
End: N/A

Check-out
Start: 9:12 a.m.
End: 9:14 a.m.

Total visit length: 105 min.
Value-added time: 55 min.
Non-value-added time: 50 min.

Figure 3   A simple process map for data collection.

the waiting time between steps is drawn as a triangle. The time at which each step started and ended is recorded, as well as the wait times between steps. Adding up the times at the end of the patient visit, as shown in the total visit length, value-added time, and non-value-added time, presents an overall picture of how the clinic is functioning. Most often, this is a picture that very few people in the clinic have seen.

You may notice that there is a lot of downtime during your observations, while the patient is waiting for the next process step. Use that time to look for wastes in the process. Are the staff members walking back and forth from work areas to exam rooms? Where are staff members located—with the doctor, or in a separate area? Are exam rooms well organized and clean? Do physicians or others leave exam rooms to get supplies or information? Challenge every time the patient has to move from room to room, or to a testing area, or to another function like scheduling. Can that service move to the patient instead? When patients are waiting, ask yourself why.

Share your observations with the team to create a sense of urgency for the changes to come. Like Dr. Han, most physicians, and often their staff as well, are surprised to learn how little time their patients spend with the doctor relative to their overall time in the clinic. The information you collect through observation makes a compelling case for improvement efforts precisely because it represents real data rather than opinions or perceptions.

WASTE

In any complex system, and in many healthcare processes in particular, wastes are rampant and represent an important opportunity for improvement. Some wastes can be dealt with quickly, and some require a more deliberate approach.

Lean defines *waste* as any activity that takes up resources but provides no value. Obvious examples include waiting time, walking to retrieve supplies, searching for missing information, duplicating steps performed earlier in the process, or exceeding the necessary steps. The most common wastes encountered in outpatient clinics are *waiting* and *motion*—by both workers and patients. An example of this is the X-ray department being far from an orthopedic clinic, or a blood drawing center being separate from a clinic exam room. This results in multiple "wait states" for the patient, poor handoffs or transfer of information, and much movement of the patient from one provider of service to another. Each provider is also unaware of how each of the other steps is proceeding, so coordination of how the patient flows through the steps is impossible. Variation of provider cycle times—the conundrum for all health care efficiency efforts—leads to long waits between steps and wreaks havoc on the patient experience.

With more detailed knowledge of your own process, you may also detect another common waste—overprocessing. Examples include excess paperwork, dictation of reports that are not likely to be read, and obtaining unnecessary tests. Many of these are a result of policies that are established by institutional requirements, for which flexibility is lacking, or, more commonly, are not explored for greater utility. For example, an ophthalmic imaging protocol for patients included tests embedded in the process that the physician and her team had initially thought might be helpful when they established the protocol, but the results of which had not been used by anyone for years. Although it only took two or three minutes extra per patient, the cumulative effect of imaging 50–70 patients per workday over the course of four years resulted in wasting thousands of hours of technologist time and that of physicians who awaited test results before deciding treatment.

Direct patient observations are an excellent way to see waste in the process. Wastes can also be identified through interviews with staff members, and through mapping the process. By far, the most important step in effecting change is to watch patients going through the process and learn to see it through their eyes.

A big obstacle to eliminating waste can simply be physicians who are used to doing things a certain way and have a hard time envisioning doing things differently. For instance, it is hard to become efficient if a physician persists in showing up late to the clinic, or if she refuses to relinquish control of patient flow to others in a better position to handle it. For physicians, we can often quote the cartoon *Pogo*: "We have met the enemy, and he is us!"

WORKLOAD DISTRIBUTION

Now that you have the process data in hand, the next step is to use them to develop a clear picture of the clinic operations. There are several key measurements that are necessary to an overall process understanding, including the following:

cycle time—The amount of time necessary to complete a process step (like check-in, or the physician consultation).

takt time—The amount of time that each process step must take, on average, to meet demand.

percent load—The percentage of the total work in a process distributed to a given process step or worker.

changeover time—The time required to change from providing service for one patient to the next. It is the time between services when nothing of value to the patient is happening. If a physician provides care to a series of patients, each minute of changeover is a minute less of his utility.

The concept of takt time is particularly important to understand. *Takt time* is an expression of the rate of consumption for a particular process, and tells us the pace at which a process needs to perform in order to meet demand. It is a mathematical fact that is independent of cycle time, number of workers, or number of steps in the process. For a clinic process, it is calculated by dividing the time available to see patients by the number of patients scheduled. For instance, in a 3.5 hour (210 minute) clinic with 21 patients scheduled, the takt time is 10 minutes (210 minutes ÷ 21 patients = 10 minutes). With that takt time, any process step that takes longer than 10 minutes on average will fall behind and cause a bottleneck. Therefore, the work involved in the care delivery process must be distributed such that no one member of the care team has more than 10 minutes of work do to with each patient. Otherwise, the process will not perform fast enough to meet the demand, and the clinic will fall behind, causing patients to wait.

Because the physician is the main constraint in the system, it is most likely that the physician's consultation time or activities between patients (changeover time) will be the steps that exceed takt time and cause bottlenecks. The simple step of observing and timing the physician's process relative to takt time would immediately highlight problems in the process.

The physician's process time must also be compared to the work content of each of the other members of the care team. Do all team members have approximately the same workload in the process? Or are some steps more time-consuming than others? The amount of work (and therefore time) that each team member is assigned in a process is called the *percent load*. Ideally, the work of the entire process should be evenly distributed so that each role can be performed within takt time. Inefficiency is a certainty for any process in which the workloads are unevenly distributed. Fortunately, it only takes one or two clinic sessions for an observer to detect inequities in workload, providing another reason to begin with direct observation of the process.

DR. HAN'S STORY: LEVELING THE PATH TO PROGRESS—A CASE STUDY

The following example illustrates workload redistribution for my outpatient procedures clinic, in which I administer to a series of patients skilled injections of a very expensive medication into a critical organ. Screening, imaging, and surgical prep must be performed prior to the injection.

In this clinic example, demand for services requires that 10 patients undergo the procedure per hour of clinic time. Therefore, takt time is 60 minutes divided by 10 patients, or six minutes. In this clinic, patients are registered at the front desk (three minutes) and instructed to sit in a waiting area, are met in the waiting area by a technician who brings the patient to an examination room for a screening evaluation (10 minutes), receive imaging tests (11 minutes), undergo preparation of the surgical field and instrument setup (four minutes), receive a minor procedure (here, a medication injection), and are counseled on postoperative care by the physician (six minutes), then are discharged (one minute). The distribution of work at these various steps is shown in Figure 4. A standard form is used to record staff and physician cycle time.

In the current state, the screening and imaging portions of the process have the longest cycle times. The rapidity with which any of

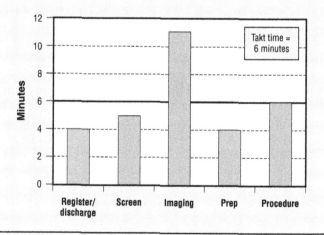

Figure 4   Percent load chart prior to intervention.

Continued

Continued

the other steps are done would thus have little impact on through-put. In theory, because imaging takes the longest time (11 minutes), it would be the limiting factor on the number of patients (about five) that could be treated within a one-hour time period (60 minutes divided by 11 minutes/patient equals 5.5 patients). However, if 10 patients were scheduled per hour, there would be an accumulation of patients at each of these steps.

In a future state in which higher throughput of patients were to be obtained, interventions with both screening and imaging would be required. An examination of resources here is appropriate. In this example, resources include a receptionist for registration and discharge, two technicians who do both screening and surgical preparation, one imaging technologist, and one physician.

The presence of two screening technicians rather than one has an immediate impact on workload leveling. With two technicians doing screening and surgical preparation, the average screening time is effectively cut in half because they only do half the number of patients (10 minutes divided by 2 technicians equals 5 minutes), and the average prep time drops to 2 minutes (4 minutes divided by 2 technicians). Had there been a third technician, the effective screening time would decrease to 3.3 minutes (10 minutes divided by 3 technicians). But because the physician workload is more than that of each technician (6 minutes versus 5 minutes), only two technicians are necessary.

Yet, the cycle time for imaging of 11 minutes poses a bottleneck. Obtaining a second imaging technologist and associated equipment would be an obvious solution. However, the cost of adding such resources was prohibitive, so there were only two other options: reducing the length of the imaging cycle time, or reducing the frequency of imaging. Both were investigated. A thorough review of the clinical trial literature and polling of medical experts in the field indicated that imaging could be reduced by two-thirds with no clinically significant effect on outcomes. A protocol was established for less-frequent imaging based on established clinical need. In lean jargon, the waste of *overprocessing* was thus identified and eliminated. In theory, the average amount of imaging time for the entire patient group could thus be reduced to one-third of the original because two-thirds of patients would no longer need imaging. In reality, there was high variation because some patients needed

Continued

Continued

imaging and some did not. For illustrative purposes, Figure 5 shows a new and reduced cycle time of 5.5 minutes (11 divided by 2 equals 5.5) for imaging. At this point, the workload distribution appeared as shown in Figure 5. Finally, root cause analysis identified that there were occasionally prolonged wait times for imaging because the equipment was periodically used by another physician's clinic simultaneously. The procedure clinic was switched to a different day of the physician's weekly clinic template for better access to imaging. This led to further efficiency gains.

According to the new workload distribution in Figure 5, the procedure has become the limiting factor on patient throughput. In theory, the number of patients that could be treated per hour is now 10 (60 minutes divided by 6 minutes/patient equals 10 patients). At this point, interventions to reduce the procedure cycle time, even by small amounts, are likely to result in increased throughput.

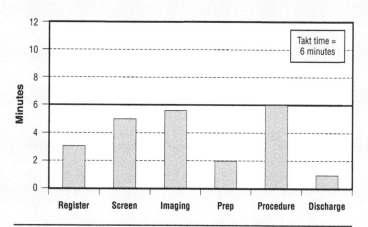

Figure 5   Percent load chart after initial intervention.

2
Visually Manage the Patient Process at the Front Line

DR. HAN'S STORY:
STUCK IN A SILO

I was continuously frustrated and puzzled by a common occurrence in my clinic. I would be working continuously and smoothly early in the clinic, and I was ready for the patients as they became available. There was no one waiting for me. "This is going to be a great day," I thought. "No backups here." Then, late in the clinic session, I would find several patients ready for me all at once. At that point, the patient waits were established. I was instantly "behind," there was no time to adjust, and we almost always finished late. Our clinics were notorious for being behind at around 11:00 a.m. each day. I felt powerless because there was not a way for me to improve the situation by changing my own pace. Several of my physician colleagues complained of the same problem. I did not realize that this was the result of a passive system. We had no mechanism by which we might recognize the need for intervention before the delays became established. We had no idea that such a tool existed—the clinic whiteboard. Furthermore, the idea that we could dynamically adjust our process was even further from our ken. We needed two things simultaneously—an active process and a tool to enable it—and neither would work without the other.

My puzzlement remained until I read a classic example in Goldratt and Cox's book *The Goal*. We were like a troop of Boy Scouts hiking a trail in single file, with a slower hiker anywhere in the system slowing the pace for everyone behind him. The Scouts would arrive at their destination with the first Scouts spread apart and way

Continued

Continued

ahead of the rest, followed by a group bunched up behind the slow hiker—like the batch of patients being ready for me all at once. As in their process, dependency and variation were rampant in ours, and we needed a way to deal with them. It's funny: as a former assistant scoutmaster for a Boy Scout troop, I had seen this hiking scenario several times, yet I had never made the connection with my own workaday world!

The patient observations described in the last chapter help a clinic team understand the current state of its processes and define the patient flow gear in the center of the synchrony diagram (Figure 1). In this step, we will discuss the main methods of adjusting the pace of that gear to keep it in synchrony with the physician: visual management via the patient status whiteboard, and a multifunctional clinic team. Visual management is the key to knowing what adjustments need to be made to the pace of patient flow; a multifunctional team makes those adjustments happen.

The goal of visual management is simple: to communicate the status of the entire clinic at any given moment quickly and easily to all team members. This means creating a visual management tool that is centrally located, visible at a glance to all staff, and easily updated. A visual tool that clearly communicates the status of every patient in the clinic puts the emphasis on the actions the team needs to take to move the patient through the process. A well-designed visual tool makes intuitive sense to the care team, and becomes something that the team cannot work without.

PASSIVE SYSTEMS FOR PATIENT FLOW

At the outset, transitioning to visual communication feels a bit unnatural precisely because it is so radical a change from the previous system. That is because most clinics operate passive systems for managing patient flow rather than the active system that creates synchrony. To determine whether a clinic system is active or passive, ask these questions:

- Is there a lot of walking by your staff or patients?

- Do you use the size of a pile of records in a bin or a list of names on a computer screen as an indicator of patient flow?

- Are the persons delivering care in one step of your process oblivious to how the other steps are proceeding such that they cannot provide assistance without someone having to call it to their attention?

- Is there any time when patients in your clinic process are out of sight and out of mind by even part of the clinic staff?

- Is the physician often interrupted by phone calls about emergencies and scheduling of patients?

- Are there periods when clinic staff members wait while the physician is behind?

- Do clinic workers do a set number of functions that change little, even when patients are waiting?

- Is there an indifferent attitude toward small inefficiencies?

If you answered "yes" to these questions, the clinic is using a passive system and would benefit from a visual communication tool that would allow for active adjustments to the care process.

If you answered in the affirmative, you are not alone. Most clinics manage patient flow passively rather than actively. In a passive system, patients go through the process without consideration for when the physician or other providers are ready for them, and without regard for their time as a valued resource in the process. Two telltale signs of a passive clinic system are a chart bin (physical or electronic) for indicating patient readiness, and a process full of "silos" of activity.

Chart bins or routing slip systems use the physical appearance of a patient's chart or slip in a bin as an indicator of the patient's readiness for the next step in the care process. Electronic systems can also act as bin systems; in this case, the indicator is a colored button on screen next to a patient's name rather than a piece of paper in a bin. Either way, patients may wait because there is no active coordination based on anticipated visit length or patient needs. This happens because the default mechanism is to take the patient at the top of the list or chart bin no matter what the situation. There is also no mechanism that actively triggers the next step to occur, further exacerbating patient waiting.

For example, in one obstetrics clinic, the receptionist created a routing slip for each patient, walked the slip to the medical assistants' workroom, and attached it to a clipboard that hung in the hallway outside the workroom. The sound of the clipboard was the signal for the MAs that a patient had checked in and was ready to be called back and have vitals taken. The patient status was also indicated in the electronic patient records system.

However, in this passive system, the MAs had to refresh their screen to see the patient status or listen for the sound of the clipboard; if they were not in the workroom, they did not see the screen nor hear the clipboard. To make matters worse, since the walk to the MA workroom was 80 steps, the receptionist often waited to make several routing slips before leaving the desk to hang them on the clipboard, creating a bottleneck before the process was even under way. The MAs then had no opportunity to actively adjust the process to accommodate the batch of patients sitting in the waiting room. In this clinic, wait times were high, and so were staff and physician frustration levels.

Electronic records that contain signaling features have reduced the need for physical movement to initiate steps in a process. But they cannot communicate the optimal timing of steps, or in what order or for which patient those steps need to be performed. This is because the vertical listings of patients in an electronic record do not provide an understanding of how quickly patients will pass through various steps in the process, some of which may differ between patients. Such an understanding is needed for active coordination of patient flow to the physician or other process constraints, such as imaging or casting. Furthermore, even with electronic records, there are physical constraints that are often underestimated—the clinic worker must be at a computer workstation to see the signal, and the workstations around the clinic are often occupied with the task of recordkeeping. There is no simultaneous and continuous understanding among team members as to what is happening with patient flow. In a simple process, without variation in visit length or testing requirements, signaling through the electronic record may be sufficient. However, in more complex systems, multifunctional teams need to be informed when to move from one function to another, and where the team members are located at any moment in time. Electronic records are usually ill suited to the task.

Passive care systems are also prone to operating in disconnected silos. *Silo* refers to care that is applied in a service-centered fashion—with services like check-in, radiology, and casting operating independently—rather than a patient-centered one (see Figure 6). In many clinics, persons delivering care in one step of the process are unaware of how the other steps are proceeding, and so are unable to provide assistance to the workers in other steps. Usually, this is because they are not expected to do so, have not been trained, or do not have the means or infrastructure to communicate with each other. Physical barriers or distance may separate them. Value is thus added in silos of activity, where the workers are isolated from each other. In this model, patients move from station to station, often with waits in between. Delays at any one step accumulate and affect the patients that follow.

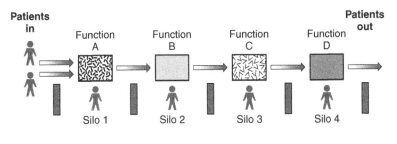

Example functions: Limitations:
A. Tech screen   • Backup at any one step will slow everyone down
B. MD exam, scribe   • Poor visibility of workers to each other
C. Imaging   • Patient and staff motion to and from waiting area
D. Procedures   • Wait states are programmed

Figure 6   Silo effect from processes performed in series.

How do you know if a silo system exists? It takes but a few minutes to see, even if you are unfamiliar with the clinic you are observing. One quick way is to look at how patients are tracked through the process. If a pile of records in a bin is used as an indicator of patient flow, and there is no shifting of worker activity to reduce each pile, a silo of activity exists. In the electronic medical record system, it is the accumulation of patients in a list on computer screens at various workstations without a dynamic process of reducing the length of the list by workers at other stations. Another sign is the inability to locate patients in the process, indicating difficulty in communication between workers as to a patient's progress and whether expediting is needed. Also, if some workers are standing around while others are falling behind, it is a sure sign that dynamic shifting of human resources is not occurring. Somewhere, someone needs help, otherwise they would not be waiting. But who needs the help and where? Visual communication boards act as a radar display in an air traffic control tower, playing a critical role in coordinating patient flow to the physician in an even, nonoverlapping fashion.

PROBLEMS WITH A PASSIVE SYSTEM

There are many problems with a passive system. First, there is no direction as to how to arrange the order in which a patient might proceed through evaluation steps. Even if there is no dependency between those steps, there is no ability to direct patients around bottlenecks, nor is there a way to recognize when the need arises for such intervention. Secondly, the record is often placed beneath other records that have arrived earlier in the bin, and so the order of the bin does not indicate priority; neither do the listings on the computer screen. As a result, there is typically limited coordination or rearrangement of patient order to minimize overall wait time. Finally, a pile of records or a lengthening list is interpreted as a slowing of flow, but in actuality is worse than that—it is an indicator of established delay. These delays are in the making even before the pile forms, outside the awareness of both the physician and staff, and there is no mechanism in place to recognize what is occurring until it is too late. In other words, by the time the staff sees the pile, patient flow has actually stopped. If you were to compare patient flow to a river, a backwater has developed in which patients are no longer moving. For them, flow has stopped.

One of the biggest problems for patients, though, is that in passive systems patients are both waiting and visible to each other for much longer periods of time. In a waiting room full of patients, those people know who has been waiting longest and who has just arrived. Anything longer than a few minutes between steps is an invitation for a patient to make comparisons with other patients' waiting time. So, the staff may be reluctant to actively rearrange patient order because of the fear that an earlier patient might be offended if he sees a later patient taken ahead of him.

Passive systems also pose problems for members of the care team. When people work in silos, they are often not empowered to step in and assist in another area, even when the bottleneck is obvious. As a result, there is little opportunity for job enrichment, and employee engagement and satisfaction can wane. But an active system based on a multifunctional team gives people the chance to expand their skill set, feel more engaged in both the work and the improvement process, and participate more fully in the care process. We have observed many workers ask to be transferred to physician teams that provide this engagement, even in the same clinic environment, and with the same resources and level of compensation.

THE PATIENT STATUS BOARD

To solve the problems presented by a passive system, the care team needs to understand the entire process and be able to see that process in action from beginning to end. Once the team knows not only how many patients are scheduled for the day and how many are already in the clinic, but also which patients are at what step in the process and where delays are likely to occur, they can begin to take action to even the flow, remove bottlenecks, and keep both the patient and physician moving through the process. Visual communication via the patient status board is the critical tool for providing that knowledge.

In our experience, the simplest tool is the best for creating a patient status board, and so a low-tech magnetic whiteboard is a good choice; an electronic whiteboard works as well. A whiteboard is typically inexpensive, and so can be purchased by the clinic manager without many layers of approval, and does not need involvement from an IT department to install. It can be designed and hung in a visible spot in an afternoon, reinforcing the immediacy of the improvement changes that the team is empowered to make.

To design the patient status board, use the data collected during the patient observations. During the observations, you drew a box for every process step and timed both the process step and the wait time between steps. Those steps become the columns on the patient status board. On a magnetic whiteboard, magnets with patient identifiers move across the columns to indicate where in the process each patient is located, and who from the care team is with which patient. The magnets can be color coded to indicate the patient type as well. Most clinics stack up the patient magnets for the entire clinic day as an indicator of how many patients are on the schedule. Figure 7 is an example of a typical patient status board. The patient

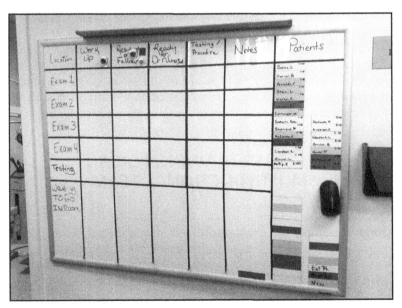

Figure 7   Patient status board.

status board lists the exam rooms down the left column, and the process steps across the top. By moving a magnet labeled with the patient identifier across the columns as the patient moves through the process, the care team can actively manage resources and maintain flow.

The board answers the following questions for the clinic team:

- Which patient is in which room at any given moment?

- Is it a new, follow-up, post-op, or another type of patient?

- Who is with the patient?

- In which step in the care flow is each patient?

- How many patients are waiting for a particular resource (like the physician or radiology)?

- How many patients remain on the day's schedule?

- Are there cancellations or no-show patients today?

- Is the clinic ahead or behind schedule?

The answers to these questions provide the information the team needs to make the active adjustments to the process needed to achieve synchrony. For example, knowing that there is a new patient in one exam room and a follow-up patient in the next helps the team direct the physician to the follow-up patient first and avoid long wait times (see Dr. Han's anecdote at the beginning of Chapter 1.). Knowing that a physician, nurse, or medical assistant is with a patient in a particular exam room eliminates the guesswork of finding a team member when needed. And knowing how many patients are left on the day's schedule helps all team members set the pace of work. The actions the team can take based on this information are the throttle levers represented on the synchrony diagram (Figure 1).

CROSS-TRAINING FOR A MULTIFUNCTIONAL TEAM

The team can be even more effective in adjusting the flow of the patient process when they are cross-trained and multifunctional. When patient magnets are stacked up in a particular column of the patient status board, it becomes visually obvious that a bottleneck is developing and delays will begin to accrue. If team members are multifunctional, they can step in to help alleviate the bottleneck and keep the flow of patients constant.

In Dr. Han's clinic—and indeed in clinics everywhere—bottlenecks commonly formed when all four exam rooms were full with patients waiting for Dr. Han to be ready to see them, and more patients were waiting in the waiting room. The root cause of this problem was the disparity between the amount of time it took the technicians to do their part of the care process and the amount of time required for the physician consultation. The technicians routinely finished their part of the process more quickly than did Dr. Han, and then piled up patients in front of the doctor. In lean we call this *overproduction*, when one part of the process works too quickly and overwhelms the next step in the process. In order to turn overproduction into synchrony, the two steps need to work at the same pace.

In this example, the technicians spent an average of seven minutes to work up a patient, while Dr. Han averaged 10 to 12 minutes in the patient consultation. The solution to this imbalance was to cross-train the technicians to assist the doctor in the exam room in the extra three to five minutes the technician had available between patients. The technician assisted with documentation, answered some patient questions, and escorted the patient out of the exam room.

The cross-training of technicians had several important benefits. First, two or three minutes of the physician's work content was transferred to the technician for each patient, freeing up 40 to 80 minutes of patient consultation time during a busy clinic day. Secondly, the technician no longer had the opportunity to "stay busy" by working up the next patient and creating a bottleneck. In other words, the technician's part of the process fell into step with the physician's part of the process. With no bottlenecks, the clinic end times became more predictable and patient wait times, defined by the amount of time the patient sat idle, dropped by more than 50%. Finally, the technicians began to feel more valued and utilized in the clinic as they learned more about the diseases being treated and could proactively assist the physician.

DEPENDENT AND PARALLEL STEPS

Cross-training is one way to build flexibility into the clinic process and keep the flow of patients steady; another strategy is to analyze the process for dependent steps that could be made parallel. *Dependent steps* are ones that are performed in a certain order, in which one is a prerequisite for the next, while *parallel steps* can be done in any order. Often, care team members assume that all of the steps in their process are dependent, when in

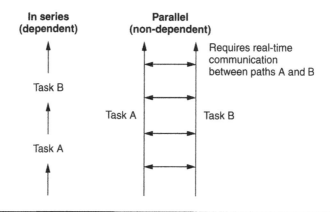

Figure 8   Dependent versus parallel steps.

fact they have simply been performed in the same order for so long that they appear to be dependent when some could be parallel (see Figure 8). To build a flexible and responsive process, investigate whether the process allows for any parallel steps.

For example, in Dr. Han's clinic, patients were required to have their eyes dilated before the rest of the exam began. However, the clinic team found that photography could be done either before or after the physician's exam, giving the team an option to keep patients flowing even when the physician or the photography area was already busy.

DR. HAN'S STORY: THE BOARD SPEAKS

On the first day we used the patient status board, I began to understand its power. I had two technicians working with me, and 18 patients to see in three and one-half hours. I could see from the board which patients were in the clinic, and could use that information to pace myself. I could also see potential bottlenecks forming—but so could my team. They were able to make adjustments to keep patients moving because they knew which steps were going to take longer or could be taken in a different order. They could assist me or work up new patients depending on the flow in the

Continued

Continued

clinic. When patients fell behind in the process relative to their appointment times, they were visible and could be expedited. It was also immediately clear whether patients could be directed to me rather than to photography if the photographers were busy. It did not take long to make these decisions.

I never had to ask anyone, "How many more patients are there?" or "What happened to Mrs. Jones?" Even better, no one asked me, "Which patient do you want me to put in a room first, doctor?" I do not like that question; it's not a decision I want to make. But now, I could look at the board and anticipate my work.

We finished the clinic 15 minutes early that first day—something that had never happened before. One patient said to me, "That's the shortest I've ever had to wait here, and I've been seeing you for 20 years!" I didn't know whether I should be insulted or, like my patient, gleeful. I didn't work any faster than before, and I did everything I usually do for my patients—I gave them the best care I can. But I realized that focusing solely on my own activity in a physician-centered approach was not sufficient. I had to synchronize my activity with patient activity to see these kinds of results, and the patient status board was the key to doing that.

3

Adjust and Control the Gears for Synchrony

DR. HAN'S STORY:
THERE'S THE RUB!

Understanding my process well enough to synchronize it with the patient flow only took 30 minutes of my time. With Aneesh as my facilitator, I mapped out my process in detail, with steps as granular as "I walk to the door of the exam room," "I review the record," and "I open the door to the room." As I walked through my process steps, I began to think about the need for certain supplies and equipment in the exam room and my own movement in the exam room, and began to see the value in mapping out the examination and changeover process so thoroughly.

The next step was to estimate how much time each of those steps took, an exercise that highlighted both to me and to Aneesh just how much time documenting the medical record takes, and how much it distracts from my process of patient care.

Finally, I had to estimate how often each step was accomplished without a hitch. That made obvious the sticking points in the examination process, and what impact correcting each problem would have on the overall system.

During the next clinic session, it was clear that the team had used my process information to make some simple yet impactful changes to the process. I was not interrupted during patient examinations by phone calls or missing equipment. In fact, some of the instruments I needed for specific patients were placed where I could see them, when I needed them. I never thought I would see the day when that would happen. That day, the clinic ended early—something that was becoming a more regular occurrence.

Continued

Continued

> My team also helped to solve the problem of the time required for documenting the medical record. The two technicians on my team often had extra time while I was wrapping up with a patient, and so, as a trial, they began to step into the exam room as they were available. From that trial, we developed the role of the scribe. The technician/scribe would accompany me into the exam room, take notes during the consult, assist if I needed help or materials, and escort the patient to the lobby at the end of the exam. This saved me up to four minutes of time in each exam, which added up to 45 minutes during the half-day clinic. I could see another patient, return phone calls, or even have a lunch break.

Now that we have come to understand and actively manage the patient gear on the synchrony diagram (Figure 1), it is time to do the same with the physician gear. Both of the gears on the diagram can be adjusted with "levers" worked by a multifunctional staff, and we have discussed the levers that control patient flow: visual management, cross-training, and parallel steps in processes. In this chapter, we will discuss the tools available to adjust the physician gear: *changeover, pods,* and *workplace organization.* We need to focus on physician flow at this point in the process because no matter how adept the care team is at adjusting the patient flow, synchrony is impossible if the physician is not available when the patient is.

There are many reasons why the physician would not be available while the clinic is running. There may be a routine delay in getting the first patients scheduled in the clinic ready to see the physician, creating an expectation that the physician has time to do other things while the clinic gets started. Once in the clinic, the physician might not know which patient is ready to be seen, or which is the highest priority to be seen first. Missing information, missing team members, and missing supplies all take the physician out of the exam room, sometimes in the middle of an exam, when a patient is least likely to tolerate the interruption.

The physician is a *shared resource* in the clinic, which means that while there may be more than one nurse or medical assistant in the clinic, there is typically only one physician, and every patient needs to see her. Shared resources are bottlenecks in the process. As such, their time must be spent providing value, and the non-value-added tasks must be eliminated or shifted to other resources. But what is non-value-added? The physician might disagree that returning a phone call or e-mail is a waste of her time. The key to determining waste in the physician process is to put every action in the context of synchrony: does this action help the physician to be available when the patient is?

For some actions, the answer to that question is obvious. A physician leaving an exam room for supplies or equipment does not help her be available when the patient is. A physician trying to decide which patient is next to be seen does not help achieve synchrony; nor does a physician who works in an isolated office and has no view of the overall workings of the clinic. These are wastes in the process; in order to achieve synchrony and bring the patient and doctor together at the same moment, those wastes must be eliminated.

CHANGEOVER

Changeover refers to the amount of time and the steps performed from the time the physician is finished with one patient exam until the time he begins the next patient exam. In lean terms, changeover prevents the shared resource—the physician—from continuing to provide value. Since shared resources are bottlenecks in the process, they should be providing value continuously in order to prevent delays in the system. So, the goal in examining the physician's changeover time is to eliminate the unnecessary steps and move as many of the remaining steps as possible to the rest of the staff. Once that occurs, the physician can move more seamlessly from one value-added patient interaction to another.

In Dr. Han's anecdote at the beginning of this chapter, changeover included documenting the medical record and escorting the patient to the lobby at the end of the exam. Both of these steps are necessary and so are not the kinds of wastes that can be simply eliminated. However, it does not follow that Dr. Han had to be the person completing these steps. Having a technician available to act as a scribe and escort patients out saved time for the shared resource (Dr. Han) without compromising the quality of care.

To understand the physician changeover process, start with a process map. The physician should list in detail every step he takes from the time that he finishes seeing one patient until he begins to see the next. In this exercise, the actual patient consultation is not the object of study as that is the value-producing step, and lean focuses primarily on non-value-added activity. Here, we are not looking for ways to make the patient consultation more efficient; instead, we are looking for sources of waste to remove from the process as a whole so that the physician has more time—in a calmer environment—to spend face-to-face with the patient.

Once the steps are listed, estimate the amount of time each one takes. In a lean system, the value-producing step—the patient exam—represents the majority of time the physician spends in the process. The process is raising a red flag if the shared resource is spending more time on something other than patient consultation. Among those steps that do not directly provide value, are there any that can be assigned to other resources in the clinic? Can the team members be cross-trained to assume tasks as needed to keep the physician flow in synchrony with the patient flow? Evaluate every step in the physician process for the possibility of improvement.

Finally, look for the problems in the process by noting how often each step is completed correctly, without errors or omissions. Does the physician always have the information, equipment, and supplies he needs? Which steps in the process are the most problematic? The answers to these questions will tell the team where to focus their problem-solving and improvement efforts.

Armed with this information and analysis, the physician and his team can design a changeover process that keeps the physician flowing from one value-added activity to the next, utilizes the staff to their fullest potential, and provides the patient with the best possible care.

PODS

The space in which a physician and her team are working has a big impact on how the team communicates and how quickly they can adjust to each other's needs to create synchrony for the patient. Synchrony requires coordination between the physician and staff members, often on a minute-by-minute basis. The space in which that team works must be designed to allow for that coordination and communication, without waste.

That the layout of a work space can lead to waste may be a counterintuitive notion. But if the physicians' and staff's workrooms or offices are remote from the exam rooms, then practically every patient encounter requires excess walking. This simple waste of motion has a deep impact on the system as the staff may not feel the urgency of preparing or seeing the next patient, especially if the physician is also tucked away in an out-of-sight office. When the team cannot see each other and the process in action, the focus is taken off the immediate needs of the patients, and wastes and waits take over. Imagine a pit crew with separate offices two minutes away from the racetrack: with every step away from the locus of action, readiness diminishes. Even if there is great communication on the team, separate offices and workrooms result in excess walking and add unnecessary time to the process as waste has been built directly into the system.

The lean answer to the question of physical layout is a *pod*, or hub, in which the entire care team—including the physician—is colocated. When a team shares a space, communication and handoffs of information are easier and more efficient, and the waste of walking to find team members is automatically removed. Ideally, the pod is located close to the exam rooms so that a patient status board (see Chapter 2) can be seen by all, and the focus and urgency can be kept on the patient process.

There are many ways to create a pod. The simplest is to locate the physician in the same workroom with the medical assistants or technicians while the clinic is operating. This usually requires only moving or adding computer screens to accommodate the additional team members; the results are immediate visibility and higher levels of coordination.

In order for the pod to be most effective, the team working with the physician should remain as stable as possible. Once in their own space, the team needs to be able to change and improve processes in small, quick experiments; rotating staff through the team is disruptive to that effort. Clinics that do not keep a stable team around the physician lose much efficiency in the change process, and need an internal or external facilitator to continually brief the staff on the new processes in place. To create the stable base of operations needed for synchrony, dedicate a team to work with the physician, even if that team is only working together during the clinic in which the lean changes are being implemented. To be clear, dedication of a team to a physician does not mean that the team is limited to working with that physician. However, it does mean that whenever the physician works to improve his clinic using lean, that team is assigned to him. We have found that capable support staff can shift their work patterns from physician to physician more easily than can physicians shift their work patterns to those of different teams. This is altogether appropriate, as the health delivery process is, for medical reasons, unique to the physician and not to support staff.

WORKPLACE ORGANIZATION

Workplace organization—called 5S by lean practitioners—is the key to creating an exam room environment in which the physician can maintain eye contact with the patient rather than looking for supplies, leaving the room, or working on a computer with his back to the patient.

We have talked to physicians who describe not having what they need once an exam has begun and having to leave a gowned patient on the table while they call for assistance, or not being able to open a drawer to retrieve equipment without taking gloves off. The goal of organizing the exam room is to enable the physician to conduct an exam in a calm and orderly environment without these kinds of interruptions and distractions.

Supplies, equipment, and forms should be optimized like an airplane cockpit: sitting in his chair, the physician should be able to reach for whatever he needs. Ideally, the changeover process includes looking ahead to the next patient and setting up anything extra that the physician will need. Common forms should be in the exam room to prevent the doctor from leaving the room to retrieve them; supplies and equipment should be stocked in quantities sufficient for the clinic day before needing to be replenished. Everything stored in the exam room needs a place and a label so that low stock can be quickly noticed and filled. The same is true of supply cabinets outside of exam rooms as well.

Once the exam room is set up for optimal efficiency, look for ways to eliminate the need for the physician to leave the room. Is there a resource available to help with medical documentation, get an unanticipated supply item in the middle of an exam, or enter orders while the physician is outlining them for the patient? Many times, this requires some rethinking of the staff's roles and responsibilities, and some rethinking of who does what. If your clinic team already seems stretched thin, remember that as efficiencies are improved within the clinic, resources become available to take on tasks that they were not able to do before.

Efficiency gains create the flexibility and responsiveness needed for synchrony. For example, in one clinic as the medical assistant role was examined and improved, the MAs had time available to walk into the patient room toward the end of the consultation and input orders into the electronic medical record (EMR) as the physician was communicating those orders to the patient. This change accomplished two goals: first, the doctor did not have to enter the orders himself, saving a minute or two of physician time. Secondly, the communication was seamless and error-proof, and prevented the physician from having to track down an MA in the hallway after the exam to pass along the orders. This change to the MA role allowed the physician to remain focused on taking care of the patient's needs, and prevented the waste of overprocessing caused by repeating information or doing work that could be done by someone else.

4

Plan for Variation in Patient Type and Length of Visit

DR. HAN'S STORY:
MEETING THE BIGGEST CHALLENGE

As head of our vitreoretinal section, I had tried for many years to streamline our clinics. Managing the different levels of complexity of medical problems and doing it on a time budget had defied my abilities. We made many mistakes.

We began our clinic days with the more complex patients, thinking it would take longer to evaluate them, so an earlier appointment seemed reasonable. We did not group our patients according to their testing requirements or complexity levels.

Patients were seen in the relative order of their appointments, no matter how quickly some might have gotten through screening or testing. We had a principle of having technicians cross-cover more than one doctor's clinic at a time, so few got to know any one patient very well over the course of follow-up visits. How long each patient might take based on their emotional and physical needs was a mystery until it was too late to manage the situation.

The result was a predictable morass. As the clinic session progressed, the patients began to accumulate, and so did their waiting time. The doctors had to curtail their interactions with patients to get through the backlog. Long patient waits for short physician visits were common—and so were angry patients who required apologies. Attempts at making technicians and physicians more efficient with their work tasks were met with failure because any small gains were lost in the chaos of poor patient flow. We failed to manage variation and dependency, and everyone suffered the consequences.

Continued

Continued

As we understood variation better, we made changes. We no longer started our clinic with the most complex patients, but with the quick ones we could get in and out. They appreciated that. We put the more complex patients closer to the end of the clinic where they were less likely to cause delays for other patients. If complex patients were added, we made sure they were not scheduled back-to-back with another complex patient. We managed expectations, informing the more complex patients of the need for a longer visit length that also incorporated a longer period of physician counseling. We created a specialized clinic just for patients likely to require brief testing and short procedures like ocular injections for macular disease. Because leveling workloads and eliminating waste was much easier in the specialized clinic, we could do more in less time, and thus created capacity to handle more patients in both types of clinics—specialized and not. A consistent team of technicians was assembled for each physician clinic. We then could anticipate the course of each clinic session and adjust accordingly, using the active measures of synchrony.

In the synchrony diagram (Figure 1), the patient flow and physician flow gears are controlled by multifunctional staff members who are equipped to speed up or slow down the pace of either gear to keep them in synchrony. The team needs this capability because of the variation inherent in healthcare processes.

Variation is unavoidable in healthcare because of the very nature of working with people. Patients and their needs vary greatly from day to day, exam to exam, procedure to procedure. The processes are also run by people who can vary in their pace of work, energy, and attention. Variation is the biggest challenge to efficiency in almost every healthcare process.

Variation in healthcare can be defined as the differences in cycle time that can occur from patient to patient at a given process step. For example, vaccinations that take only seconds to administer to an infant or adult can take significantly longer to give to a young child who is afraid of needles. Casting technicians may take longer to apply a cast depending on the type of fracture; radiology technicians may need more time for X-rays if a lift is needed. Even simple process steps like check-in or taking vitals can experience variation in cycle times when there are complicating factors like language barriers or mobility issues. These examples are natural process variation; we expect to find this kind of variation in healthcare processes, and while we can manage and reduce it, we cannot eliminate it.

Variation has is greatest impact when process steps are dependent on each other. *Dependency* is defined as the requirement that one step be completed before another is initiated, or that patients must be seen in a particular order (see Chapter 2). Often, there is dependency in healthcare processes because information from one step—test results or images, for example—is needed in order for the next step to be performed. But quite often, dependency is the result of habit: the steps have simply been done in a particular order for so long that dependency is assumed. Upon examination, there is often room for dependent steps to become more flexible and responsive.

When variation and dependency are present simultaneously, delays mount. If one step falls behind, the time cannot be recovered when steps must be performed in a rigid sequence. This occurs even when the average workload among the steps is even, as it is more difficult to speed up a dependent process than it is to delay it. For example, imagine two patients whose appointments are scheduled 15 minutes apart. They are scheduled to first be screened by a technician, then seen by the physician 15 minutes later. If the first patient takes 20 minutes to screen instead of the usual 15, the physician is already five minutes behind by the time the first patient gets to her. All subsequent patients will wait an extra five minutes as well. If the physician takes more than 15 minutes with any one patient, all patients after that will be delayed further. Each individual delay adds to the total accumulated wait time. Even if subsequent steps are equipped to handle things quickly, the delays remain.

In essence, patients are like cars attempting to drive at the posted speed limit on a one-lane highway without the opportunity to pass slower traffic in front. The slowest car will delay all cars behind it, even if they are capable of driving up to the speed limit. If the slowest car eventually speeds up to the limit, the delays that have already been established will remain for the cars behind it because they cannot pass the slowest car, and they have their own limits on speed. In this example, the speed limit is analogous to the rate at which a worker can do the job safely and accurately. Obviously, the remedy for this situation is to create a passing lane that removes the dependency of one car's speed on that of all the cars in front of it. That passing lane is the option to do steps in parallel (side-by-side) rather than in series (one behind the other).

There are two kinds of variation in the healthcare setting that get in the way of achieving synchrony: process-based variation and patient-based variation. Both have similar effects on flow because they impact the time it takes to complete process steps. In order to achieve synchrony, the clinic team must be flexible and responsive to both of these forms of variation.

Process-based variation is built into clinic systems as the steps in the care process vary in cycle times depending on who is performing the step and who is receiving care. Examples include differences in how fast patients or staff can walk from one workstation to another (the longer the walk, the greater the variation), variation in the availability or location of supplies, or variation in the people supporting the physician. Process-based variation is dealt with by using the classic principles of lean: finding and removing the sources of waste, organizing the workplace for minimal motion and maximum efficiency, involving the people doing the work in the design of new processes to increase awareness and understanding, and communicating the status of the process to the entire team with clarity and immediacy. The team owns the process, so while this type of improvement takes effort and may require the involvement of stakeholders at many levels of the organization, process-based variation can be realistically examined and greatly reduced.

Patient-based variation is due to differing healthcare needs from patient to patient. In this type of variation, the patient's health condition and individual psychosocial factors can require radically different amounts of clinic resource use. Patient-based variation is intrinsic to healthcare and cannot be eliminated, so it must be dealt with by alternate means. There are three ways to handle such variation: isolation, diffusion, and dependency reduction.

Isolation means segregating patient types that are complex and known to possess high levels of variation and thus require more staff time and flexibility, allowing more-predictable and routine patient types to flow through the clinic unimpeded. Moving complex patient types toward the end of the clinic session minimizes the potential impact of variation during the clinic day. Alternately, some practices choose to dedicate entire clinic sessions to a particular disease family, which groups patients with certain conditions, testing requirements, and resource needs so that a process can be designed to meet those needs efficiently.

For example, scoliosis or clubfoot patients require extra time with the physician and staff to discuss complex surgeries. The families of patients need to understand the preoperative testing requirements, the equipment they may need to purchase after the surgery, or the time required to care for the surgical patient. Having these complex discussions in the middle of the clinic day will certainly throw off the flow of the clinic and cause delays for other patients. Complex patients are therefore scheduled toward the end of the morning or the end of the day; this ensures a smoother clinic flow and allows for lunch and after-clinic time to serve as an additional buffer should the consult go even longer than anticipated. In this case, the volume of the patients is low for a given physician, so a separate clinic for these surgical consults does not make sense.

On the other hand, one sports medicine clinic routinely saw concussion patients during regular clinic hours until the volume of concussion patients increased dramatically. Some of these patients, especially new patients, ran over the sports medicine slot times with the physician, causing backups for other patients and resulting in late clinic end times—and dissatisfaction for the physician and staff. Some concussion patients require specialized testing as well, further adding to delays caused by the variation inherent in this patient family. As the practice grew and the number of concussion patients increased, it made sense to create a separate concussion clinic. A full day of clinic was divided into two half-day sessions: the morning clinic remained a sports medicine clinic, and the afternoon was devoted to concussion patients. Isolating the concussion patients in this way allowed the sports medicine clinic to minimize variation, ensuring that the physician and the staff were prepared for concussion patients in the afternoon.

Patient-based variation can also be *diffused*. Diffusion is the opposite of isolation—rather than creating clusters of similar patients, here complex and variable patient types are spread out in a clinic schedule so that patients with uncertain resource needs are not scheduled near each other in the clinic day. On a diffused schedule, new patients would not be scheduled back-to-back, as major disruptions are possible when two long and unpredictable visits occur close to each other in time. Clinic staff and physicians can adjust to variation better when it comes in small doses and separated in time, and wait times do not accumulate for patients.

With a schedule that uses diffusion to manage variation, new patients are scheduled intermittently with follow-up or post-operative patients because new patients are inherently unpredictable and require more of the physician's time to both understand the patient's condition and establish a relationship. If the physician is scheduled to see a new patient and then a follow-up or post-operative patient or two, any extra time required by the more complex new patient can be made up during the simpler and less variable consultations with the follow-up patients. Repeating this pattern throughout the clinic allows the physician and the staff to develop a rhythm of catching up throughout the day, and prevents delays from accumulating.

Even if the scheduling template is designed to diffuse complex and highly variable patients, delays can still occur if too many of these patients are scheduled for any one clinic day. In the practice of one oculoplastics surgeon, those complex and variable patients had Graves disease or orbital tumors. Unlike the concussion clinic example described above, this practice did not have the volume to justify a special clinic devoted to Graves patients or those with orbital tumors, so they had to be scheduled in a way that did not bring the clinic to a halt. If that complex patient was scheduled as the first new patient of the day, and the physician needed to spend a significant amount of time in the consultation, all other patients were subject to long delays that could not be made up during the less complex appointments. The solution for this clinic was not only to diffuse the complex patients, but to change the scheduling template to ensure that only one or two Graves or orbital tumor patients were scheduled during the clinic day.

The final technique for reducing patient-based variation is *dependency reduction*, which means finding those places in the care delivery process in which steps can be taken out of order when necessary to keep the process moving. Can certain steps that are usually done before the patient sees the physician be delayed until after the physician exam? If more than one provider is involved, can the order in which they see the patient be changed? Creating this flexibility is similar to adding a passing lane in the highway analogy above—the alternate sequence (or passing lane) is only taken if the process slows down. If the physician is unavailable but an alternate step of the process is, then the process can keep moving at the speed limit (see Figure 9).

For example, in one retina practice the technicians had always taken patients for required photos after they had their eyes dilated in a workup room. If the photo equipment was already in use, this step often required moving the patient from one waiting room to another until it became available. The patient was then moved again into an exam room, further adding to the unnecessary movement and wait times in the process.

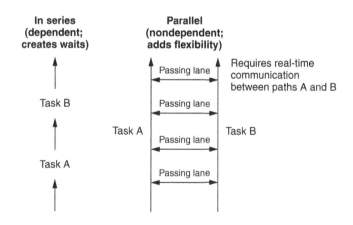

Figure 9   Reducing dependency to reduce variation effects.

The solution to this situation entailed the entire system for achieving synchrony. First, the technicians used a patient status board to immediately and clearly indicate whether the photography equipment was in use. Secondly, the practice created dual-purpose rooms for both the technician workup and the physician's exam to minimize patient motion. Thirdly, the team investigated the possibility of taking the required photos before dilation to add flexibility (the "passing lane") to the process and found that they could indeed change the order of the steps when needed. In the new process, the patients move less, and the technicians have an option to either work up the patient or have the photos taken, depending on the available resources.

Dealing with variation is the sine qua non of clinic efficiency. It is the pivotal activity through which decreased patient waiting, increased quality, and improved staff morale can be achieved. It creates an environment in which things get done efficiently and without fanfare. And it is the single most important factor in coordinating patient and physician flow, the cornerstone of synchrony.

5

The Environment for Synchrony

DR. HAN'S STORY:
WHAT GETS MEASURED GETS MANAGED

One day during our transformation I arrived in the clinic to find graphs of process performance data posted on the clinic wall next to the exam room. I was surprised at the public nature of this information: everyone could see it, including the patients. The graphs very clearly communicated how long patients in the clinic were waiting, the number of days until the third available appointment, and how many new and follow-up patients were seen each day. My team had chosen these metrics to measure our performance, but I had some doubts at first. It seemed rash to post the information for everyone to see. Our wait times especially were a matter of fate and circumstance, so why post something that couldn't be changed?

I could not conceive that tracking and communicating metrics could catalyze progress. But after several days, I saw how the technicians worked to ensure that the data were consistently positive. They took pride when there was marked improvement, and were actively involved in problem solving when the data showed difficulties. The technicians kept me engaged in value-added work by maintaining a steady flow of patients, knowing that every minute spent providing value was a minute less a patient would wait, or a minute more available to spend with a challenging or complex patient.

Making the data visible fundamentally changed the environment by empowering my team to be responsible for the process and how it performed, and allowing them to choose the measures that would define success. In the past, these kinds of improvements

Continued

Continued

> would be short-lived, lost in the chaos of inconsistent enforcement, changing priorities, and lack of feedback. But with these very visible charts and the daily performance feedback they provided, the team developed a sense of ownership for the lean changes and set the stage for sustained improvement.

So far, we have discussed how to map out, improve, and control the pace of both the physician process and the patient process. At this point on the road to synchrony, it is time to evaluate the broader clinic environment to ensure that it supports and enables lasting positive change. There are two critical elements that contribute to an environment that supports synchrony: the metrics by which the practice's performance is measured and rewarded, and the physical layout and utilization of the space.

METRICS

What a practice chooses to measure and communicate as an indicator of success has a large impact on the work environment and culture of that practice because it tells the team what the organization values. If the metrics are linked to financial compensation or other types of recognition, they will get extra attention. More than policies or slogans or programs, metrics communicate priorities.

Patient volume is a common metric and one that is linked to physician compensation and incentives, so it is a highly visible metric for many healthcare organizations. But patient volume by itself is only one facet of success; there must be other metrics that tell the frontline team how they are performing and provide feedback from patients as well. In fact, patient volumes can be seen as a consequence of performance metrics the team can impact: the better the patient experience, the more patients the practice will attract.

As the transformation progresses and the practice changes, the team should select metrics that are the best indicators of the success of their processes, and—importantly—are within the team's control. For example, the team can directly impact patient wait times, clinic end times, access, patient safety, and patient satisfaction scores. Tracking and posting these kinds of metrics on a daily basis lets the team know how they are doing in real time and provides fact-based information for problem solving.

Tracking patient wait times, clinic end times, and satisfaction scores for physicians, staff, and patients allows the practice to question the current state and build an improved and efficient clinic. The single most important metric in driving a transformation is *patient wait time*, as waiting patients are always a symptom of a larger process problem. This metric should be tracked and posted daily to keep the focus on the key element of synchrony: valuing the patient's time equally with the physician's. *Clinic end times* indicate how well the patient schedule is working, and whether add-on patients and work flows are impacting a predictable flow in the clinic day. Measuring *satisfaction scores* for staff and physicians can be as simple as asking, "How was your day on a scale from one to five?" and graphing the results over time. All of these metrics provide immediate feedback, as well as opportunities for problem solving and improvement.

Other metrics relevant to synchrony are access, patient value, and patient safety. *Access* indicates how many days a new patient would wait for an appointment with the physician, and is often measured as time to the third available appointment to buffer the effect of cancellations or add-ons to the schedule. Access tells the team how well a physician is discharging his patients, or whether there are enough clinic hours available for the patient volume. *Patient value* measures the efficacy and necessity of ordered labs, tests, and procedures, drug costs, and alternative treatments. *Patient safety* measures errors, near misses, and other variables as determined by the specialty or practice.

Once the team has established metrics important to their clinic, the process for tracking the data is relatively simple. Ideally, one person is responsible for collecting and posting the data, either at the end of the clinic or before the next clinic day. These data should then be presented on a run chart (run charts track a particular metric over time) and hung in a highly visible area where all staff—from frontline team members to administrators and executives—will see the same information. The charts must be reliably updated in order to attract and retain the staff's attention; if the information is out of date or is only sporadically updated, the very people who could benefit from the information will stop looking. The charts themselves can be created by hand, printed, or electronic. The key is to create timely, reliable data accessible to everyone in the clinic.

Including metrics beyond patient volumes in the way in which the practice is evaluated changes and broadens the team's definition of success. This change allows the physician to become highly efficient and see a higher volume of patients while also focusing on lower patient wait times and higher patient and staff satisfaction. A work environment that values both physician efficiency and the patient experience is at the heart of synchrony.

PHYSICAL LAYOUT AND SPACE UTILIZATION

We briefly looked at physical layout concerns in Chapter 3 when we discussed creating a pod for the physician and her team to increase communication and immediacy in the care delivery process. Here we will take a closer look at layout and space utilization and their role in supporting and enabling the lean processes that achieve synchrony.

Process problems and space utilization problems are often closely linked; that is, where there are long wait times and built-in delays, there are also problems with layout. That is because the process does not exist separately from the physical space of the clinic—how rooms are designated and used in part determines the process. A broken, fragmented care process—one that operates in silos of service (see Chapter 2)—is often reflected in and compounded by an inefficient layout and poor space utilization. The best transformations—the ones in which synchrony is truly achieved—change the process in concert with changing the space.

The most obvious problem caused by a poor layout is excess motion for both patients and staff. The root cause of this problem is single-purpose rooms; for example, one room dedicated to screenings or vitals, and another dedicated to exams. This builds in wait times because it makes the availability of the right room an additional constraint on the system. For example, an ophthalmology clinic dedicated one room for technicians to work up patients, and another room for the physician exam. These two single-purpose rooms created a host of problems in their clinic process. First, having two sets of rooms to manage required that two sets of resources had to be available to move the patient to the next process step, building in delays while the patient waited for the technician and the room to become available. In addition, the technicians had to scan both sets of rooms to see which was available, determine which patient should go where, and retrieve her from the waiting room, compounding the delays with excess motion. The source of these wastes and resulting delays was a poor layout and space utilization dependent on single-purpose rooms.

Excess motion can be detected through patient and staff observations and the creation of spaghetti diagrams. A *spaghetti diagram* is a basic diagnostic tool for determining wasted motion. To create one, sketch the physical space under observation, and draw a line to indicate each time a patient (or staff member) moves. The example in Figure 10 shows the patient movement in Dr. Han's clinic prior to the lean changes. In this example, the exam room, laser room, and waiting rooms are all single-purpose rooms. The patient is then required to move from silo to silo in order to complete the care process.

The goals of redesigning a clinic space to achieve synchrony are to eliminate excess patient walking and staff walking, to create a common work space for the physician and staff, and to enable a calm and orderly environment for the patient-doctor interaction. In our work with many different physicians across many different specialties, these goals result in a common list of features that support synchrony: *flexible, multipurpose treatment rooms, a central location for shared resources, and a shared workroom that colocates the physician and staff.*

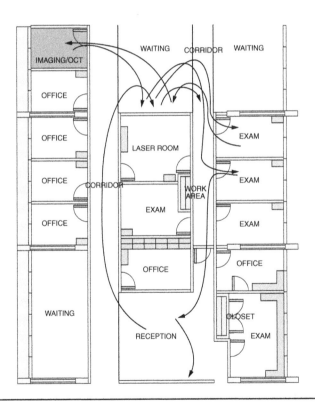

Figure 10   Patient movement in Dr. Han's injection clinic prior to lean changes.

FLEXIBLE, MULTIPURPOSE
TREATMENT ROOMS

A multifunctional, cross-trained team can add flexibility and responsiveness to a system dependent on single-purpose rooms, as any team member is able to intervene at any step in the process. The team can see where delays are occurring (with visual communication, see Chapter 2), and dynamically shift their activity to move the process along before delays accumulate and affect the entire clinic. Figure 11 illustrates this concept: while the rooms can accommodate only one function, each team member is capable of performing all functions.

Process flexibility is much greater, however, if that multifunctional team is working in a space with flexible treatment rooms. A flexible treatment room might function as a tech workup room, a vitals room, or an exam room, as needed. They are the equivalent of the "passing lane" discussed in Chapter 2, as they remove the constraint that a dedicated room imposes on the process, and allow a multifunctional team to keep the process moving

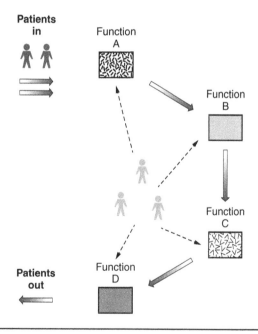

Figure 11   Multifunctional team/single-use rooms.

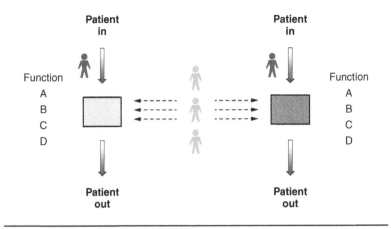

Figure 12   Multifunctional team with flexible treatment rooms.

with whatever room and resources are available. A commonly understood example of such an arrangement is the use of labor–delivery–recovery–postpartum (LDRP) rooms by many obstetrics services. Figure 12 shows the combination of multifunctional team members with flexible treatment rooms. Not only can the team members perform all necessary functions, the rooms can be used for all functions as well.

A flexible treatment room can be further enhanced by making supplies and equipment mobile. Often, needed materials are not too cumbersome to be brought to the patient in the room, or stored there on carts. For example, in an orthopedic clinic, the examinations, blood draws, medication injections or treatments, casting, and discharge instructions can all be done with mobile equipment in a flexible treatment room, thus eliminating both wait times and excess motion.

CENTRAL LOCATION FOR SHARED RESOURCES

In reality, complete multifunctionality of workers and space is not always possible. Highly specialized tasks may need to be reserved for specific workers with specialized training. Some equipment may not be easily moved, even with a cart, and so must remain stationary in its own room and require patient movement. In such cases, that equipment is considered a shared resource and should be centrally located to prevent excess motion on the part of patients and staff. The more regularly that equipment is used, in fact, the closer to the action it should be located.

For example, in Dr. Han's clinic, the optical coherence tomography (OCT) equipment is specialized and not mobile. The photographers are also specialized, and the task of taking photographs cannot be shared with the technicians. Clearly, a multifunctional team using multifunctional rooms would not work for the OCT equipment. But the original location of the OCT equipment meant that the technicians and the photographers spent excess time walking between their work areas to search for and retrieve patients. The team created a spaghetti map of the photography process, and discovered that the layout was causing an extra 40 to 60 minutes a day of walking (see Figures 13 and 14). Add to that the excess walking required of patients and the delays built into the process, and the case for moving

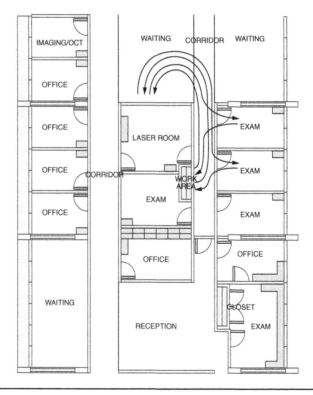

Figure 13   Technician movement before relocation of OCT equipment.

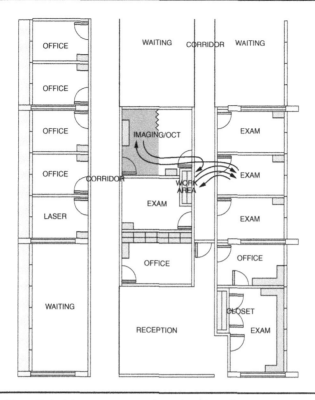

Figure 14   Technician movement after relocation of OCT equipment.

the OCT equipment was clear. The team moved the photography equipment to a room closer to the exam rooms, where—although it remained a single-purpose room—proximity allowed for better communication and less wasted motion.

In another example, a practice kept the refrigerator for medicines in a room used for procedures. While that room was centrally located, every time a medicine was needed, the team had to check whether the procedure room was occupied and potentially wait until it was free to retrieve the medicine. This space utilization had the effect of making one patient wait through another patient's procedure in order to finish the care process. The team relocated the medicine refrigerator to a small room—previously a sub-waiting room—that provided a good view of the doctors' offices and exam rooms. They decided to locate the technician workstation there as well. The move solved two problems for the technicians, giving them access to the needed medicines, and allowing them to better keep an eye on exam room availability as well as patient and physician motion in the clinic.

SHARED WORKROOMS THAT COLOCATE PHYSICIANS AND STAFF

The example above makes good use of available space but stops short of the best solution for creating the constant communication, flexibility, and responsiveness to variation that synchrony requires. Even better than being able to see the physicians' office is being able to share the same work space. Shared workrooms bring the physician into the same room with his support staff, allowing for better and more efficient handoffs of information, more visibility into what needs to be done next and by whom, and how the process needs to be adjusted to keep the patients in synchrony with the physician.

Shared workrooms for physicians and staff are not the norm in healthcare today. Most commonly, we have seen physicians in one work area or in separate offices, medical assistants or technicians in another workroom, and even a third area for nurses. Each layer of separation builds delays, missed communication, and, potentially, errors into the process as team members look for each other, hand off information in hallways, or fail to connect. Interpersonal relationships between physicians and staff are difficult as well with separate work areas, as there is little opportunity to talk socially. Those interpersonal barriers then create barriers for the free exchange of ideas in the clinic, preventing open discussions about problems and improvements.

A shared workroom can be created in an existing space, and often requires little more than adding a computer to an existing workroom to enable the team to work together during the clinic. In Chapter 3 we discussed creating a pod for the physician, at least during the clinics in which the lean changes are being made. A pod is essentially a shared work space, even if that work space only temporarily accommodates the whole team. Physicians do not need to give up their offices—the goal is to locate him with the staff while the clinic is running.

A pod or temporary workroom will help improve the team communication that is necessary to keep the patient process in synchrony with the physician process. This achieves the goal of a shared work space with minimal walking for everyone and visual awareness of empty or full exam rooms and staff status at any given moment. However, this kind of pod is often close to patients entering and exiting exam rooms. If a patient stops to say hello to the physician or a staff member, she is unwittingly causing a disruption to the flow that can result in delays. Providers are then put in the awkward position of trying to conduct a social conversation while also maintaining synchrony for the other patients in the clinic.

Privacy is also a challenge in any traditional design with a long hallway of exam rooms, punctuated by a physician workroom on one end and staff workstations somewhere in the middle or at the other end of the hallway. Often, exam rooms are not soundproofed, so patient conversations can be heard by the other waiting patients. The team also has to be extra careful about what information (especially other patients' images or EMR records) is displayed in the open on the terminals located near the hallways. In this environment, it is difficult to create an efficient physician and patient flow due to disruptions, interruptions, and workers slowed down by the patient traffic patterns.

An extensive clinic remodel, expansion, or new construction provides a valuable opportunity to incorporate synchrony into the very design of the clinic and allow process improvement to inform the space design. The practices we have worked with typically choose to improve their processes first, and then bring that deep knowledge of their own patient care process to the task of designing the clinic. This work results in clinic spaces that meet the specific needs of each clinic precisely, but which have some elements in common.

The most important of these common elements is the combination of flexible treatment rooms and common workrooms in a "hub and spokes" model. The hub is the common workroom—the command center for running the clinic and maintaining synchrony (see Figure 15). This hub contains the patient status board, supply cabinets, medicine refrigerators, and equipment carts, as well as computers and space for each member of the team. Sometimes the work spaces themselves are counter high so that team members can work standing up. This work area is removed from patient sight and traffic, which allows the staff and physician to work with fewer disruptions and more privacy.

From this central hub, the staff and physician can enter any of the flexible treatment rooms—the "spokes" in the model (see Figure 16). In the best designs, the patients enter those same rooms from a separate hallway, keeping the noise and activity of the workroom out of view and making a calmer atmosphere for the patient experience. In this model, both patients and staff walk less, so delays are reduced or eliminated. Patient privacy is also improved, as there are no hallway information handoffs for patients to overhear.

There are some costs in approaching a clinic remodel or new construction with synchrony in mind. The first is time. In order to design a space

Figure 15 Common work area in the hub-and-spokes model in an ophthalmology clinic.

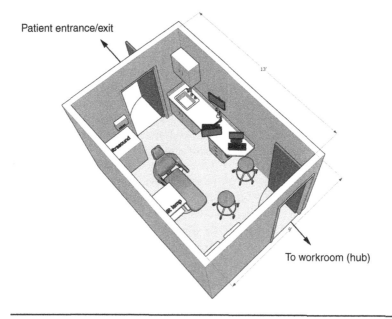

Patient entrance/exit

To workroom (hub)

Figure 16 Floor plan of exam room in an ophthalmology clinic using the hub-and-spokes model.

with the specific needs of an improved process in mind, the team needs to invest the time to observe, map, and understand the process. In our experience, that process adds a month to the design phase of a construction process. Secondly, the hub-and-spokes model involves duplicating hallways and doors for exam rooms, which can be a counterintuitive notion for architects.

But as the delays are removed from the system, clinics find that they can increase their patient volumes with the same or fewer treatment rooms. An ophthalmology clinic in Michigan that underwent this process added 30 to 45 minutes of capacity to the clinic, or between three and five additional patients per day. Add to that the increased satisfaction of patients, staff, and physicians, and the investment in planning for synchrony pays off.

6

Techniques for
Change Agents

Much of what is described in the preceding chapters is the factual,
actionable science of achieving synchrony. But if you, the change
agent, are responsible for making these kinds of changes in a
healthcare organization, you know that the science of synchrony—and of
lean—is only half of the story. The other half of the story is change management, and it is a force to be reckoned with, whether that change is being
guided by an external consultant or driven by an internal team or facilitator.

If you are an internal change agent—quality manager, lean facilitator or coach, trainer, organizational development specialist—this chapter is
for you. You have the special challenge of making change happen through
other people, and so must understand not only the concepts and tools of
lean needed to achieve synchrony, but also techniques for working success-
fully with groups of people who may or may not immediately see the need
for change.

As you go through the steps for achieving synchrony, the challenges
you face in managing change evolve. Issues we commonly encounter at
the beginning of a transformation—if dealt with properly—are no longer
a problem once some progress has been made a few months into the lean
work. New challenges arise at each phase of the project; each one can dis-
tract from or even derail the synchrony process.

We have organized our experience managing the change process in
a clinic setting along the timeline of a typical road to synchrony. In the
beginning of the project, the change process involves relationship building
while uncovering issues and observing the care process in action—tasks
that often cause discomfort in the project team. Team members who are
uncomfortable can react poorly to the prospect of change; physicians are no
exception in this regard. Mid-transformation, real process problems begin
to surface and need to be solved in ways that keep the effort focused on
both the patient's and the physician's time. Along the way, lean coaches and

facilitators have to be prepared to address tough questions about strategy, including how lean works with electronic health record (EHR) systems, and how the organization may have to change to support lean. We will address each of these challenges in turn.

Be aware that no two clinic processes are identical and that each one carries its own challenges. The chronology of clinic transformation may differ from one clinic to another, and even from one physician team to another. Nevertheless, we have found that a common sequence of steps, depicted as a stepladder, provides a workable template for transformation (see Figure 17). In this example stepladder, each step builds upon gains achieved in the previous step. An important caveat: many of these steps can occur in a different order or concurrently with each other depending on your clinic environment. The sequence of steps as we present it here is a good starting point; use your observations and knowledge of the clinic and team to modify it as you go along. The example stepladder was used to implement major transformation in Dr. Han's clinic over a period of months, with change trials occurring for one clinic day about twice per month, giving time to adjust to new work flows in between.

Note that the stepladder incorporates the introduction of lean concepts to the clinic team. This book can serve to introduce such concepts and augment supplemental lean training for physicians and staff that can speed the change process. The subsequent discussion continues from this point.

AT THE BEGINNING OF THE TRANSFORMATION

Your first task is to observe the patient and physician flow and collect data. But even people who are excited to be part of the lean work will be nervous with someone standing in the hallway taking notes and timing their work. So, be sure to spend time with the team first, introducing yourself and taking time to establish a relationship before jumping into your observations. Make sure everyone on the staff knows who you are, what you are looking for in the observations, and how the information you collect will be used.

As you conduct patient observations (see Chapter 1), you should also make the following observations:

- How often do staff walk from a workroom to exam rooms? How often do they walk from one area of the clinic to another? How many steps do the staff members take during a typical patient visit?

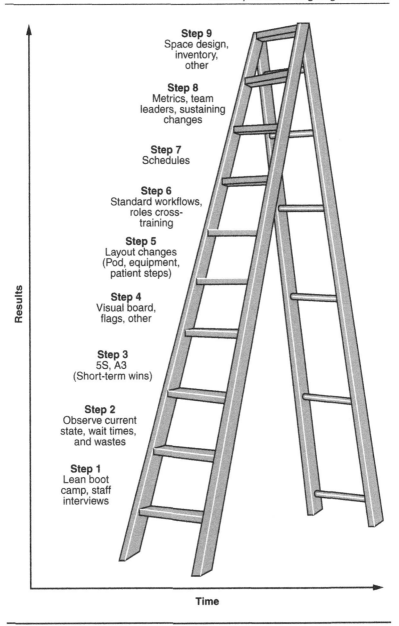

Step 9
Space design,
inventory,
other

Step 8
Metrics, team
leaders, sustaining
changes

Step 7
Schedules

Step 6
Standard workflows,
roles cross-
training

Step 5
Layout changes
(Pod, equipment,
patient steps)

Step 4
Visual board,
flags, other

Step 3
5S, A3
(Short-term wins)

Step 2
Observe current
state, wait times,
and wastes

Step 1
Lean boot
camp, staff
interviews

Results

Time

Figure 17   The implementation stepladder for Dr. Han's clinic.

- What is the doctor's flow of work? When she comes out of an exam room, can she tell clearly where she should go next, or is she searching for a staff member, or looking down the hall at the closed exam room doors, or looking for something on the computer?

- Who is waiting (what staff member) at the work area when the doctor is in with another patient?

- How are people working? Do they know what to do next? Does it seem like things are under control, or do they often come back to the work area and flip through paperwork or charts? Are priorities clear, or do they have to figure things out minute to minute or hour to hour?

- How is the team situated? Is the physician seated with the team or in a separate office? How do team members communicate with each other or find each other during the clinic?

- Are exam rooms well organized? Are supplies clearly labeled? Can you tell at a glance if anything is missing? Are certain rooms (especially supply rooms) messier than others?

- Are there projects that lend themselves to an early win?

This is also the time for you to form your theories about what the main problems are and what can be done in the clinic to solve them. How can visual communication help? Where is the team located, and where might they end up moving? How might the physician get some help in the exam room during the crucial patient interaction?

A word of caution, however. Frontline teams in many organizations are buried with initiatives; often, they have had consultants both internal and external tell them what to do before. While you need to have a working theory about what needs to change, your primary job is to listen to the staff with an open mind. As Suneja often says, "I want people to see what I'm seeing and come to their own conclusions." In other words, ask the questions, challenge the assumptions, but let the team drive the changes. Do not underestimate the difference between the team implementing actions that they themselves have conceived versus those that have come from an outside change agent.

At the beginning of the project, the physician seldom knows how long it takes her to see a patient; nor does she know what steps the patient has already been through in the clinic and how long each step takes. The same lack of overall process knowledge applies to the frontline staff and managers of a practice. At this point, share the data you collected in your initial observations, including clinic start and end times, number of patients seen, types of patients, physician time with the patients, the time patients spent with people other than the physician, and the patient's overall time in the clinic compared with his or her time spent with the physician. Present the data to the physician and the team at the same time to create a sense of urgency for the lean work and inspire the group to take the first steps needed to achieve synchrony.

Getting a team going on a lean transformation requires essentially the same elements in just about every clinic, and those elements are indispensable. Start small. This means that a physician picks a practice (a half-day or a full day of a clinic) that she will focus on to create synchrony. This also means that the team that interacts with the patient before, during, and after the physician consult must be invited to the table. When all parties have been invited, team time has to be created in the schedule for the lean work. The team will need regular meeting time for the initial training as well as for ongoing project planning and observations. In our experience, that time must be designated in the staff schedule.

The initial training session should include success stories from your organization (if lean work is occurring in any other departments or areas) and basic lean concepts and tools, such as value, waste, value stream mapping, and 5S. We recommend including exercises and simulations to get participants moving and interacting with each other. End the training with a team action planning session to put the concepts into action with a "quick win" project (like applying 5S to an exam room).

Short-term wins are important for everyone to feel good about the changes. Help the group identify up to five ideas for improvement, eventually settling on two or three items to create these short-term wins. These early stories are important to create a sense of momentum for peer-to-peer communication. At this early time, 5S is the best tool that Suneja has found to further engage the physicians and the staff. Exam rooms, supply closets, hallways, front desks, and other areas are great to 5S at this point, especially when the physician is a participant in this activity with the team.

QUESTIONS TO KEEP IN MIND

If you are having trouble building momentum in the project during this stage of the transformation, ask yourself the following questions to diagnose the issues and move forward:

- Are you starting small enough, preferably with a champion physician?

- Did you create a sense of urgency by measuring and sharing data about your patient wait times, focusing on decreasing wait times?

- Have you sought input from everyone on your team, understanding that there may be skepticism and resistance to the changes?

- Have you ensured that everyone—from the physician to the frontline staff and management—has a firsthand understanding of all the steps involved in patient care and who does what?

- Did you do an initial 5S project to build early success and pave the road for future work?

- Have you created time for the team to meet, learn, plan, and reach consensus on the desired results?

- Did you create an environment in which failure is safe, running trials for short periods of time to experience, reflect on, and tweak the suggested changes as needed?

IN THE MIDDLE OF YOUR TRANSFORMATION

Once the project work is under way and the initial excitement has turned into the realization that the process is going to experience significant change, change management becomes even more critical. You are no longer making the case for change and helping the team understand their own processes; now you might be dealing with the need for organizational changes, active resistance to change, and conflict. In general, your job at this stage is to enable the frontline team to make the changes that they think are appropriate based on their lean training and expertise. Enabling the team means communicating frequently with the managers and executives who are sponsoring the project (or who are directly responsible for the area). The goal is to remove roadblocks and pave the way for smooth implementation of the team's changes. Help the team map out changes and conduct small experiments during the clinic to test out ideas and get feedback.

At this point, what you do not have to do is solve every problem or come up with the perfect process, no matter how tempting it is to take over the project work. The frontline team has the intimate knowledge of the work flows, and will buy into changes that make sense given that knowledge; therefore, they simply *must* be the ones to generate ideas, test them, and adopt them as the new process. The coach's job is to create the larger environment in which that team-driven creativity can thrive.

TEAM LEADERS

One of the ways facilitators can help create that environment is to advocate for a specific organizational change: the creation of the *team leader* position on the team. Achieving synchrony requires that a single person—a team leader—has a view of both the physician flow and the patient flow, as well as the ability to direct resources to synchronizing those flows. One person can provide direction and oversight, and very importantly, that person is not the physician. The physician is a shared resource that must be providing direct value to patients for as much time as is possible; he is not an appropriate person to coordinate the flow in the clinic. (For more on team leaders, see Suneja's book *Lean Doctors*, ASQ Quality Press, 2010).

The team leader plays a distinctly tactical role in the clinic, ensuring that the clinic environment is one that will support synchrony. A team leader role can be helpful to a team of any size. To prepare for the clinic day, the team leader proactively consults with clinic schedulers to eliminate overbooking, or places add-on appointments in the schedule where disruption is least likely, and formulates with clinician and schedulers a strategy that minimizes bottlenecks and maximizes throughput. The team leader accomplishes this through strategic template design that eliminates or isolates variation and facilitates rapid loading of the system. She also receives telephone calls that do not require physician-to-physician contact, coordinates readiness of clinic equipment, supplies, and work space before and after each clinic, and prepares the clinic whiteboard.

Once the clinic is under way, the team leader manages the flow of patients by:

- Directing technicians/scribes to activities facilitating physician or patient flow

- Determining the order of patients to be seen by the physician, depending on appointment time of patient, expected length of face-to-face time, and other patients in process

- Directing patients to ancillary tests or physician exam depending on patient and clinician flow

- Managing clinic whiteboard for visual communication to the work team

- Maintaining a continuous and steady flow of work for the physician; keeping the first-in, first-out (FIFO) lane occupied (an arrangement of rooms that visually indicates which is next for the physician)

- Scheduling same-day urgent add-on patients so as to minimize impact on scheduled patients.

- Coordinating special aspects of a patient's next visit upon discharge from the current visit.

The team leader can be assigned at the beginning of the project work to assume the role, or could grow into the role during the lean transformation. Good candidates for the team leader position can often be identified by their previous work and level of function. In most clinics, there are a few key individuals on whom the clinician has already come to rely for his or her coordination skills, reliability, and work ethic, and who have acquired respect from peers because of a sense of fairness and good interpersonal skills. Their direction of coworkers toward various activities would be honored because they lead by example. However, candidates must also be flexible and open to new ideas. The candidate must be able to voice concerns and recommendations to all involved, and to sustain a working relationship with the physician that is characterized by mutual respect.

In many cases, the capacity exists in the clinic system to create the team leader role. If you have clinic staff waiting for patients or the physician to become available, then staff time already exists in the system. In addition, as you eliminate waste and balance workloads among staff, time becomes available for a staff member to assume this role.

A team leader is a great resource for determining cross-training needs and conducting such training with the team. As the keeper of the patient status board, she will see where bottlenecks routinely occur, and can develop members of her team into the multifunctional staff members synchrony requires. For example, one team leader in an ophthalmology clinic took on the responsibility of cross-training herself, as she saw bottlenecks appearing in imaging intermittently throughout the day. She worked with her manager to learn how to do the imaging so she could personally help prevent patient wait times at this step.

Team leaders can also help determine which metrics are most important to the practice, and maintain charts with process feedback (see Chapter 5). For example, after every clinic, one team leader measures the clinic end times, number of surgeries scheduled, patients discharged to primary care, time the first patient left the clinic, and other metrics. Once a month, the team leader reviews the data with her peers and the physician. The staff discusses action items, suggestions, and improvements, and decides which ideas to trial in the practice.

WHEN CHANGE IS UNDERMINED

A team leader that manages a patient status board and works with a flexible staff can provide the coordination and direction needed to achieve synchrony. But what if you encounter resistance to getting all the pieces for synchrony in place? And what if the very people who most need synchrony are the ones who are standing in the way?

Sometimes it is the physicians who are the most effective at hindering change. Dr. Han understands that dynamic. He had hoped that other physicians in the Eye Institute would make similar gains, but not all did. Not all physicians are flexible in their work practices, or willing to let others help them improve their processes. The physician is an authority figure in the clinic and can make or break the transformation by infusing it with a spirit of collaboration or extinguishing it with his need for control.

Both physicians and managers can exhibit behaviors that undermine change. Physicians might not make time in their schedules for team meetings, and so be unaware of and uninvolved in changes and issues. They may not be open to the team's ideas or willing to give up control. Physicians and managers can be uncomfortable with a bottom-up approach to improvement, or simply fail to follow up on action items. Watch for these behaviors, and bring them to the attention of the stakeholders involved.

Dr. Han has advice for change facilitators who encounter resistance from physicians. Know first that physicians are an autonomous group, and not accustomed to being told what to do, especially by people outside the clinic setting. They need to know how the changes will impact their ability to see patients in a calm and predictable environment, what will change about their process, and what will remain under their discretion. Explain to physicians that the changes are iterative and will be tested in trials in order to decide whether to adopt or abandon them; in other words, no change is permanent unless the team decides it should be.

Finally, offer opportunities for physicians to learn about using lean to achieve synchrony and have their questions answered before any project work begins in their own practice. Dr. Han gave a grand rounds conference on the topic of synchrony in which he showed hard data on increased revenue, decreased patient waiting times, and high patient satisfaction from his own clinic. For some, the numbers spoke louder than words. The question-and-answer session was animated, as most of the doctors were hungry for more information. Those that embraced the change and were willing to try new things were the ones that succeeded.

ANOTHER SPECIAL ISSUE: EHR

The electronic health records mandate poses a unique challenge for organizations that also want to achieve synchrony. Both of these initiatives are large changes; we do not recommend trying to manage both implementations simultaneously. We recommend optimizing your processes with lean first, and then ensuring that the records system fits and supports your improved process. Change requires flexibility; in our experience, it is more difficult to change a process when the electronic tool is built for the old process rather than the evolving one.

Many physicians report that the increased requirements for documentation consume time that would otherwise be used seeing patients. The use of scribes to reduce physician keyboarding time and to increase face-to-face physician-patient time is an issue of debate. Managers seeking to sustain or enhance practice revenues face the choice between having physicians use their valuable time for documentation, incurring opportunity loss for higher patient volume, versus engaging other personnel to perform this task, which incurs its own cost. Practices under pressure to reduce cost are hard-pressed to hire additional staff. Lean can provide extra staff time to accommodate this need. One example is the incorporation of a scribe function into the tasks of a multifunctional worker. In most environments, this can be done with a consistent team and a period of training for both physician and staff. Whatever the case, remember that using lean to achieve synchrony will create capacity in the clinic and allow the provider and staff to recoup lost time from increased documentation.

QUESTIONS TO KEEP IN MIND

In the middle of your transformation, use the following questions to analyze your progress and keep the project moving forward:

- Have you established a consistent team and a space around the physician (Chapter 3)?

- Could you isolate the team in a pod or another area to avoid excessive noise and nonproductive conversations with others?

- Have you ensured that each team member can visually assess (without excessive movement or confusion) the whereabouts of others and the expected next steps for each patient at all times?

- Did you set up the exam rooms, supplies, and space in a way that reduces wasted motion for the team?

- Does the patient have to move from one room to another (for example, from a tech-only room to a physician exam room) for the sole purpose of seeing a different person?

- Does the patient have to move for photos or other tests?

- Can the next appointment be scheduled within the room (rather than at the front desk)?

- Can vitals be taken within the room?

- Have you thoroughly examined who does what with each patient (without unplanned repetition of tasks, activities, or questions)?

- Does the staff use visual signals to notify each other of the patient's readiness for the next step?

- Is important medical and nonmedical information communicated from one person to the next in a synchronized manner?

- Can the staff work concurrently with the MD and do orders in parallel?

- Can the staff scribe for the MD or assist in other ways without reducing the flexibility of workers to do other things as they become necessary?

- Can the staff prepare documentation or supplies to ensure that minimal time is spent by the MD doing these non-MD tasks?

- Can the staff learn other tasks (such as imaging, basic examination tasks)?

- What does the staff move for, and how far is that supply or information located (can things be moved closer or change made to reduce motion)?

- Have you optimized schedules and templates?

- Can you maximize the physician's available time for patient care, for example, by removing excessive reaching for equipment or supplies, waiting for computers to start, waiting for charts or images, rooming the patients, repeating orders to techs or staff, escorting patients, and so on?

7

Conclusion

In this book you have encountered *synchrony*—a means to bring physicians and patients together without waste or delay, a fundamental of clinic flow. It is both a way of constructing your processes for maximal benefit and a way of thinking that should color every intervention you might conceive. It does so by valuing both physician and patient time equally *without compromising on one at the expense of the other*. Synchrony is achieved by matching the dual flows of physician and patient through the application of lean principles, thereby reducing waste and managing variation ahead of time before the clinic starts, and on a minute-by-minute basis during the clinic. Your mission is clear: to educate your staff, to observe your patient process from start to end, to visually manage it at the front lines, and to create a dynamic team that moves to where it is needed, when it is needed.

You will certainly encounter challenges—no efforts at change are without them. Each change will have positive and negative consequences, and handling them will require foresight and persistence. By creating the proper environment for change, you can handle its human aspects, and build on your gains in a logical fashion while causing a minimum of chaos. Informing your staff that any change trials are reversible and listening carefully to what they say can go a long way toward keeping you moving forward and in the right direction. And you should continuously seek to improve, as today's solutions often lead to tomorrow's in an environment of constant change.

What should you expect from achieving synchrony? You will see it first as freed up time for the physician, staff, and patient. From this time comes value. For physicians and staff, it can be in the form of improved access to patients and a higher level of quality and safety. For patients, it can mean a caring experience in a calm and reassuring environment.

Finally, be appreciative of your frontline staff at every step along the journey. They are the crucible of change and the core around which you will build synchrony. They should be acknowledged and reaffirmed for their efforts at every turn. Celebrate their successes in a concrete way. With *synchrony*, you and your team will *make your clinics flow.*

Epilogue

DR. HAN'S STORY: A PERSONAL NOTE

This journey to synchrony has been a personal one for me. In the old system, I was tired and approaching burnout. It seemed that on a day-to-day basis in the clinic I was challenged by forces that were out of my control—by fate and circumstance that often interrupted my ability to provide the kind of care that my patients deserve and of which I know I am capable. Some days, things were relatively smooth and we didn't get too far behind; but other days were difficult, with upset patients and a frustrated staff. Worst of all, as a team, we couldn't put our fingers on what could change a day from quiet to disastrous. The late days and high stress took a toll personally and professionally.

My clinic's transformation mirrors my own. As we got rid of the waste of motion and effort and the processes became clear, so did my view of the good I could do as a physician. As the team members worked to better understand each of their roles in providing care, we each connected with our purpose for being there. And as we worked to achieve synchrony and provide exactly what the patients needed, I reengaged with those patients and ended my clinics feeling fulfilled and gratified. My patients were grateful, too—and they did not hesitate telling others about their experience.

I know I am not alone in feeling the stress of modern healthcare. Physicians everywhere are facing full schedules and increased documentation demands that require long hours to manage. And when the very processes by which we deliver care are fragmented into silos and are ineffective, we add frustration to an already demanding job.

Continued

Continued

The path forward that we have laid out in this book can change all of that. *Synchrony* means that you have what you need at your fingertips, that you are surrounded by a capable team who is working to create an environment in which you can focus on truly great patient care, and that the patient's time is valued as much as your own. Everyone benefits.

Good luck on your journey.

Index

The Knowledge Center
www.asq.org/knowledge-center

Learn about quality. Apply it. Share it.

ASQ's online Knowledge Center is the place to:

- Stay on top of the latest in quality with Editor's Picks and Hot Topics.

- Search ASQ's collection of articles, books, tools, training, and more.

- Connect with ASQ staff for personalized help hunting down the knowledge you need, the networking opportunities that will keep your career and organization moving forward, and the publishing opportunities that are the best fit for you.

Use the Knowledge Center Search to quickly sort through hundreds of books, articles, and other software-related publications.

www.asq.org/knowledge-center

Ask a Librarian

<u>Did you know?</u>

- The ASQ Quality Information Center contains a wealth of knowledge and information available to ASQ members and non-members

- A librarian is available to answer research requests using ASQ's ever-expanding library of relevant, credible quality resources, including journals, conference proceedings, case studies and Quality Press publications

- ASQ members receive free internal information searches and reduced rates for article purchases

- You can also contact the Quality Information Center to request permission to reuse or reprint ASQ copyrighted material, including journal articles and book excerpts

- For more information or to submit a question, visit **http://asq.org/knowledge-center/ask-a-librarian-index**

Visit www.asq.org/qic for more information.

ASQ®
The Global Voice of Quali

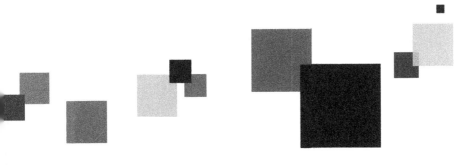

elong to the Quality Community!

ablished in 1946, ASQ is a global
nmunity of quality experts in all
ds and industries. ASQ is dedicated
he promotion and advancement of
lity tools, principles, and practices in
workplace and in the community.

Society also serves as an advocate
quality. Its members have informed
advised the U.S. Congress,
ernment agencies, state legislatures,
other groups and individuals
ldwide on quality-related topics.

sion

making quality a global priority, an
anizational imperative, and a
sonal ethic, ASQ becomes the
nmunity of choice for everyone
o seeks quality technology,
cepts, or tools to improve
nselves and their world.

ASQ is...

- More than 90,000 individuals
  and 700 companies in more
  than 100 countries

- The world's largest organization
  dedicated to promoting quality

- A community of professionals
  striving to bring quality to their
  work and their lives

- The administrator of the
  Malcolm Baldrige National
  Quality Award

- A supporter of quality in all
  sectors including manufacturing,
  service, healthcare, government,
  and education

- YOU

it www.asq.org for more information.

AINING CERTIFICATION CONFERENCES MEMBERSHIP **PUBLICATIONS**

The Global Voice of Quality®

ASQ Membership

Research shows that people who join associations experience increased job satisfaction, earn more, and are generally happier*. ASQ membership can help you achieve this while providing the tools you need to be successful in your industry and to distinguish yourself from your competition. So why wouldn't you want to be a part of ASQ?

Networking

Have the opportunity to meet, communicate, and collaborate with your peers within the quality community through conferences and local ASQ section meetings, ASQ forums or divisions, ASQ Communities of Quality discussion boards, and more.

Professional Development

Access a wide variety of professional development tools such as books, training, and certifications at a discounted price. Also, ASQ certifications and the ASQ Career Center help enhance your quality knowledge and take your career to the next level.

Solutions

Find answers to all your quality problems, big and small, with ASQ's Knowledge Center, mentoring program, various e-newsletters, *Quality Progress* magazine, and industry-specific products.

Access to Information

Learn classic and current quality principles and theories in ASQ's Quality Information Center (QIC), *ASQ Weekly* e-newsletter, and product offerings.

Advocacy Programs

ASQ helps create a better community, government, and world through initiatives that include social responsibility, Washington advocacy, and Community Good Works.

Visit www.asq.org/membership for more information on ASQ membership.

*2008, The William E. Smith Institute for Association Research

The Global Voice of Quality